World University Library

The World University Library is an international series
of books, each of which has been specially commissioned.
The authors are leading scientists and scholars from all over
the world who, in an age of increasing specialisation, see the
need for a broad, up-to-date presentation of their subject.
The aim is to provide authoritative introductory books for
university students which will be of interest also to the general
reader. The series is published in Britain, France, Germany,
Holland, Italy, Spain, Sweden and the United States.

A.C.S. van Heel and
C.H.F. Velzel

What is Light?

Translated from the Dutch
by J.L.J.Rosenfeld

World University Library

McGraw-Hill Book Company
New York Toronto

© Mrs H. G. van Heel and C. H. F. Velzel 1968
Translation © George Weidenfeld and Nicolson Limited 1968
Library of Congress Catalog Card Number 67-24448
Phototypeset by BAS Printers Limited, Wallop, Hampshire, England
Printed by Officine Grafiche Arnoldo Mondadori, Verona, Italy

Contents

1 Propagation

1 An innocent question

What is light? The question seems innocent enough, and so it is, as long as you do not ask it of a physicist. After all, any layman knows that light is 'when you see something'. But the physicist is not satisfied with such a simple answer. He tries to describe phenomena in such a way that a rational, or at least a useful, summary of observable facts is obtained, in other words a description with which he can work. By this we mean that there is a good chance that resultant predictions will provide a 'picture' of reality.

Let us take as an example the falling of objects. If we hold an apple up in the air and let it go, we are pretty sure that it will fall, at least if we perform this experiment on earth. Ever since Newton's speculations on this topic men have described it in terms of a general attractive force which all bodies exert upon one another (in our example the earth and the apple), and which we hold responsible for shortening the distance between them.

The success of this general law in predicting the orbits of the planets in our solar system, of the moon about the earth, and of the several moons about their own planets, leads us to believe that this particular method of description has put us on the right trail.

Even though it has transpired that the original idea, the original 'model' is not completely satisfactory, that a 'wider' or 'deeper' or 'more refined' framework is necessary, we can in many cases still work with the simple law of attraction.

The purpose of these introductory remarks is to make it clear that in answering the question 'What is Light?', we shall talk in terms of thought-constructions, or 'models'.

These can sometimes be easily visualised but, at other

Figure 1a. How a shadow is formed.
A straight line joining the source and
the tip of one finger passes through
the corresponding part of the shadow.
Such a line is called a light ray.

times, they can be quite abstract. For example the 'picture':
'light is to be thought of as a wave motion', is for many people
an easily visualised and helpful notion. One can also explain
and understand a great deal in terms of this model, though
unfortunately it does not explain many other phenomena, for
which another model is necessary. It will now be obvious that
in the nature of things it will be difficult to give an answer to
the question of what light 'really' is. Even deeper there lies
another question: what is truth? No physicist will be so bold
as to hazard an answer to this philosophical question. He
moves on a simple plane with, in the background, the
consideration: what can I achieve with my speculations? He
occupies himself with the construction of unifying ideas
preferably expressed in brief, mathematical form.

In what follows, we shall occupy ourselves with those
'models' relevant to our subject. We shall avoid as much as
possible the mathematical formulation and shall develop the
concepts behind the phenomena, which we must describe in
order to make possible the development of those concepts.

2 Shadows

Light moves: we receive light for example from the sun, or
from a lamp. A simple experiment teaches us something
about this motion. A source of light, so small that we can
assume it to be a point source, shines on an opaque object
(see figure 1a). Behind this object we place a white screen. We
see that a shadow is thrown on to the screen, of the same
shape as the object illuminated. We conclude from this that
light travels in straight lines, which we call *light rays*. We can
now also understand the effects which occur when the object
is illuminated by more than one point of light (see figure 1b).

We then see on the screen dark regions which no light reaches from any of the sources. There are also areas which are lit by all the point sources and between these extremes there are areas of half shadow, or penumbra, that can be reached by light from only some of the point sources.

But this model, this 'picture', of light travelling along straight lines is not good, or at any rate, not good enough. Those who have seen the sunrise in the mountains will have noticed that just before the sun comes up, the mountains in front of it are surrounded by a rim of light. This light cannot have reached our eyes in a straight line from the sun, since the sun is still below the horizon! The light bends, so to speak, over the mountain towards us. This kind of phenomenon is called the diffraction of light. Even in the formation of shadows in our first experiment something similar is going on. If one takes care to use a very small bright source of light, to put the screen a long way off, and to perform the experiment in pitch black (strange that those who study light always work in the dark, as Goethe remarked disapprovingly) then he will see that the edge of the shadow is not sharp but is made up of a number of lighter and darker bands. There are dark areas where light ought to have come in a straight line, and lighter patches where it could not have done so. This diffraction effect is not noticed in daily life because the conditions are practically never right to observe it.

3 In search of a theory

There are, therefore, occasions when light deviates from the straight path, namely when the light beams meet some sort of edge.

We must find a theory of the motion of light which also

explains diffraction effects. We have been preceded in the attempt by the great physicists Isaac Newton (1642–1727) and Christian Huygens (1629–96). Newton thought of light as a beam of small particles which are emitted by all light sources and which, when left alone, travel in straight lines, in accordance with the laws of mechanics (incidentally also first expounded by Newton). When the particles of light come in the neighbourhood of an object they are attracted towards it and change direction, so that light can reach areas which cannot be reached by straight line motion: a plausible explanation of diffraction effects.

In this book we shall come across many other properties of light, some of which cannot, without great difficulty, be reconciled with this theory. To spare us such embarrassment, we make use of another model, due to Huygens, connected with the wave theory of light. Most phenomena can be explained with it in an elegant, that is to say a short, clear and unified manner. Nevertheless, towards the end of this book we shall see that the idea of light particles has also found its place in modern physics, particularly in the description, on an atomic scale, of those phenomena which occur when light is created.

4 Huygens' principle

We now retrace, in some detail, the ideas of Huygens and his contemporaries.

Light moves, but how? Something happens in a light source and, as a result, a disturbance moves across space towards us and this disturbance is caught by our eyes. This means of motion, whereby the intervening matter seems to remain undisturbed, reminded Huygens of the following analogy

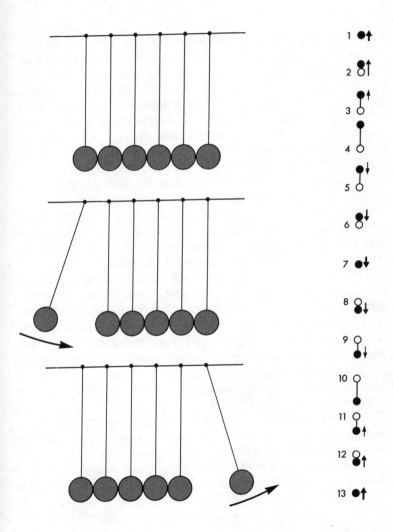

Figures 2 and 3. *Left* The transmission of an impulse. *Right* Movement of a cork on water; the equilibrium position is shown by empty circles.

15

from mechanics. Several perfectly spherical balls are strung up just touching each other. If we pull the first one away and let it fall against the second (see figure 2), we see the last one fly off, while the intervening ones stay put. This is how, according to Huygens, we should think of the motion of light, as an impulse moving in all directions of space. If the impulse starts at *P* at a given time (see figure 4) its effect at a later time will be seen in points lying on the surface of a sphere with *P* as centre. This sphere Huygens called a *front*. Later still this disturbance is found on the surface of another sphere, with centre *P*, and with a larger radius. We can think of forming the second front out of the first by taking each point *Q* of the latter to be the centre of a new impulse from which spherical fronts move outwards. The overall surface, the envelope, of these secondary fronts is the new front.

This method of constructing one wave front from another is called *Huygens' Principle*. It follows from the nature of this construction that, if one draws a line perpendicular to the first front, it will also cut the second one at right-angles. These perpendiculars originate at *P* and point in the direction of the motion of the fronts: they are nothing other than the light rays, mentioned earlier. In this way the impulse theory is reconciled with the rectilinear motion of light. But we should also be able to deal with diffraction phenomena with this theory; to do this we must first amplify it with regard to a few points. The reason for this becomes clear if we ask ourselves how the front will behave at its edge (as at *A* in figure 4). We know that a secondary front goes out from *A*. But how does this combine with other secondary fronts more in the middle, and in which direction is the light emitted at the edges? And what do we mean in this connection by the concept of a 'light ray'?

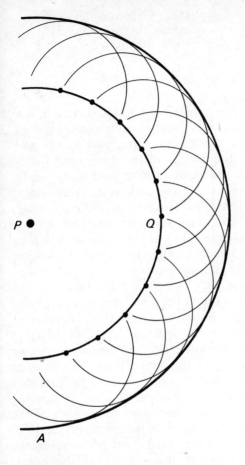

Figure 4. Huygens' method of construction to obtain a wavefront out of the previous one.

5 Waves

We shall make the necessary extension of the impulse theory, using water waves as an analogy. Indeed figure 4 makes us think of waves which move out across the surface of a pond when a particular part of it is disturbed, for example when a stone is thrown into the pond. A difference, however, between water waves and light is that the water waves move over a surface, whereas light travels in a three-dimensional space.

Figure 5. The wave at three instants in time. The crests of the wave travel to the right.

Let us follow the movement of *a point* on the surface of the water by putting a cork there. It is seen that on average it does not move sideways, the movement being mainly up and down at right-angles to the surface of the water, and therefore at right-angles to the direction of motion of the wave. In figure 3 is shown the position of the cork at different times. Empty circles each indicate the position of the cork when there is no wave; the full circles show the position, each a little later on. The speed of the cork at each time is shown by the width of the arrows. The cork undergoes a periodic motion about a middle point. Such a motion is known as an *oscillation*. After a certain number of seconds T the position and speed of the cork is again the same. The time T is called the period of oscillation. The inverse of T equals the number of oscillations per second, or the *frequency* (v). The largest displacement suffered by the cork is called the *amplitude*; we would use it as a measure of the strength of the vibration were it not that a certain ambiguity arises from the fact that the amplitude is alternately positive and negative (depending on whether the cork is on the crest or in the trough of the wave). We therefore take the square of the amplitude and call it the *intensity* of the oscillation. This is proportional to the energy of the wave. We have now examined the events occurring in one point on the surface of the water. The wave as a whole has regularly spaced crests and troughs; the distance between two crests is called the *wavelength* (λ). In figure 5 we have drawn a cross-section of a water wave through several points simultaneously, at several times. (This is really the same picture as that shown in figure 3, but taken instantaneously at several points.) Let us now look at a number of corks at *A*, *B* and *C*. In the first picture the cork at *B* has not proceeded quite as far in its oscillation as has the

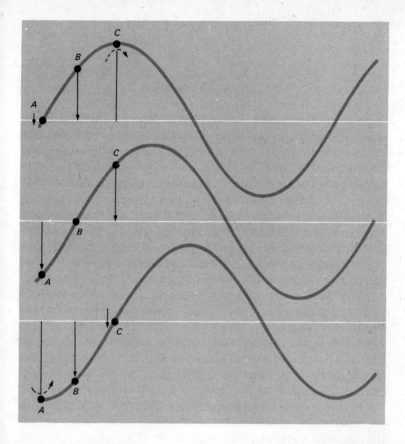

one at *A:* it is lagging in *phase*. In the next picture *B* has reached the position *A* had, but *A* has gone farther. In the third picture the cork at *C* has reached the position which *A* reached in the first and *B* in the second picture; *A* has once again started to move in the opposite direction. We see that the wave moves forward from the left to the right. The speed, *V*, with which this happens is, in homogeneous matter, equal to the product of the wavelength and the frequency, or in mathematical terms,

$$V = v\lambda$$

To simplify matters we have only described waves whose shape remains constant during the motion; such waves are called *harmonic* waves. In mathematical terms their shape is described by the sine function (*sinus* = wave), which crops up wherever waves are talked about (vibrating strings, sound, light, radio waves), and whose shape can be seen for example in a cross-section of corrugated metal sheeting. Any arbitrary wave can, at a given instant in time, be thought of as a superposition of a number of harmonic waves. The displacement at a particular point in space at that given instant in time is, therefore, the result of the displacement due to the superimposed harmonics. In figure 6 we see a wave which is made up of two harmonics which differ only slightly in their wavelength and have equal amplitudes. The triangular waveform shown in figure 7 includes an infinite number of harmonics for which the amplitude becomes smaller the smaller the wavelength. A number of components whose wavelengths are λ, $\lambda/2$, $\lambda/3$, $\lambda/4$ are shown, each with the proper amplitude.

The component harmonic waves differing in wavelength have generally each their own velocity, so that the shape of the overall wave changes with time. This effect is called *dispersion.* It must be clearly understood that the harmonic wave is a mathematical idealisation: a wave whose shape never changes during the motion can have neither a beginning nor an end. Any real wave is, therefore, made up of at least a few harmonic waves. This can, for example, be observed in the chime of a clock in which, apart from the main tone, several overtones can be heard. The collection of harmonics in a wave is called its *spectrum;* the intensities of the several harmonics are called spectral intensities.

We have already mentioned the *phase* of the oscillations gone through by a small volume of water (or a cork) at a

Figures 6 and 7. *Left* Superposition of two harmonic waves with different wavelengths. *Right* A triangular wave and its harmonic components.

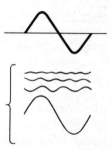

particular point in a wave. If we join points of equal phase, for example in a trough, where the maximum downward amplitude has been reached, then the resulting curve is called a *wavefront*.

In a surface of water the wavefronts emanating from a point source are circles; for light waves which travel in all directions in space we will by analogy expect spherical wavefronts. We can, therefore, identify the fronts of Huygens' theory with those of the wave theory.

6 Light waves

It will prove very useful to apply this concept of a wave also to light. We leave aside for the moment the question of what then oscillates. We just assume that energy is moving through space in the form of three dimensional transversal waves (that is to say, waves for which the oscillatory motion is perpendicular to the direction of propagation, just as in the case of water waves). We do incidentally know of another kind of wave, namely sound-waves; their oscillatory motion is in the same direction as the propagation (longitudinal waves). An important difference between light waves and elastic waves such as water, or sound, waves is that the latter need a medium through which to travel, water, or air, or a gas, while light reaches us through empty space from the Milky Way.

How large is the frequency of light oscillation? The motion of a cork on the water can be followed by the eye. In the case of light the motion is much wilder: in one second there are about three hundred million million (3.10^{14}) oscillations. The wavelength of light waves is particularly small: somewhat smaller than one thousandth of a millimeter or one thousand nanometres (nm). (One thousand nm equals about forty millionths of an inch.) Light whose wavelength is about 600 nm is seen as red light; that with $\lambda = 400$ nm looks blue. Thus wavelength and colour are closely linked.

The product of the frequency and the wavelength equals the speed of propagation. This is very large for light. In empty space it is the same for all wavelengths, about 300,000 km per second (186,000 miles per second). Since the velocity is the same for all wavelengths, there is no dispersion in space. We shall see that this phenomenon does occur in transparent media.

7 The speed of light

How can such a tremendous speed be measured? Galileo tried to measure the time to exchange light signals between two widely spaced points (figure 8). He found out that light travels so fast that the time to be measured was much smaller than the reaction time of the observers, which made it impossible to measure the speed of light in this way.

Figure 8. Galileo tries to measure
the speed of light.

23

The Danish astronomer Römer, in the seventeenth century, was the first to get an estimate for the velocity of light, *c*. Four of Jupiter's moons had just been discovered and it was known how long they took to circle their planet. Since they do not themselves emit light, they disappear from view as soon as they move into the shadow of the planet. It was noticed that in those positions when the distance between the earth and Jupiter was largest, the darkening of the moons occurred after the time predicted from the motion of the moons about Jupiter, whereas at smaller distances between the earth and Jupiter the moons were darkened too early. By measuring this difference in times and attributing it to the larger distances travelled by the light in the first case, compared with the second, Römer obtained an estimate of the speed of light.

The nineteenth century saw the first experiments carried out on a terrestrial scale (figure 9) by Fizeau. A beam of light is aimed at a mirror and the reflected light is observed. A cog-wheel rotates in the path of the beam, cutting it into small pieces. We follow, in our mind's eye, one such small piece. After it has left the opening between two neighbouring teeth of the wheel it speeds across a long way to the mirror, is reflected, and would – if only it were quick enough – run between the same two teeth of the wheel. In order to be able to tell whether this happens one makes use of a glass plate P which allows part of the initial beam a to go through and also the returning beam b, but nevertheless reflects a part c of them sideways. Such a plate is a *semi-transparent mirror*.

An observer who looks at the light beam c can then tell whether or not the returning beam has passed between the teeth of the wheel.

If the wheel is turned so fast that a tooth replaces the original gap exactly in the time it takes for the light to travel to and from the mirror, then the observer sees no light.

It is an easy matter to calculate the speed of light, from the measured speed of rotation of the wheel, the number of teeth and the distance from the wheel to the mirror. One can improve on the accuracy of this measurement by turning the wheel even faster so that the light is again allowed through, by the next gap; then faster still until the next tooth stops the light; and so on. In this way Fizeau already obtained a fairly accurate value for c.

In the early twentieth century, the American physicist Michelson made even more careful measurements. He used a rotating mirror, a method which had already been proposed and tried by Foucault in the middle of the previous century. Four mirrors forming the sides of a cube can be turned about an axis (see figure 10). Every time one of the mirrors takes up such a position that light falling upon it from a given direction is reflected towards the mirror S a long way away, the mirror S reflects the light back to the cubic mirror. In the time it takes the light to travel between the two mirrors, the cube T has rotated a small amount, so that the light reflected by T no longer returns to the point A, but is seen instead at B, a slight distance to one side. The measurement of this displacement together with an accurate knowledge of the distance between the mirrors S and T and the rotational speed of the cube, allows one again to calculate c.

Why a cube and not simply a rotating mirror? The time during which light comes back from S is short: it is only as long as the time taken by the beam reflected by T to flit across the mirror S. Therefore, only a small fraction of each rotation is effective. Hence the more mirrors one uses the better. Hence the cube. Michelson himself used up to sixteen mirrors and also made many other refinements which we shall not go into here. We will mention only that the distance ST was lengthened to 35 km (about 22 miles), that the light travelled through a tube of this length (which furthermore was pumped down to one twentieth of an atmosphere to reduce the perturbation due to air currents and movements), that the speed of rotation of the mirrors was measured to a few parts per million, that the block was made with special precision methods and that the distance ST was measured to the nearest ten cm.

Following Michelson, others have measured c, also by other methods. Nowadays the accepted value is 299792·5 km per second, with an uncertainty of 0·1 km per second.

8 Importance of the measurement of the speed of light

'Not bad', one might say. Or, with some regard for the difficulties involved and for the many complicated and precise instruments which had to be developed to obtain such an accuracy, 'pretty clever'. But why try to make such accurate measurements? Is a slightly larger uncertainty in the value of c, say 299,800 plus or minus 100, not good enough? Are we merely indulging in a childish passion for accuracy for its own sake? No, it is not just that. In this case there are several good reasons to strive for the utmost accuracy. It is not just a question of measuring one of the constants of nature, a quantity which plays an important part in much scientific and astronomical work. Nor yet is it only that once c is known, long distances on earth can be measured through a knowledge of c and the measured shift in the path of the beam B in figure 10. That is useful for geodetic surveys: a long base line is a good beginning for precise triangulation.

There is another reason, and the most important one at that. Between the different fundamental constants there exist, according to modern theory, certain relationships. Electrical, magnetic and energy units are connected in physical theory by formulae in which c also appears. The better c is known, the better also can the other constants appearing in the formulae be determined, and the better can we test the theories needed for a modern picture of the world.

9 The speed of light in matter

The value we gave for the speed of light is valid in a vacuum, but how is it affected by (transparent) matter? In connection

Figure 9. Fizeau's cog-wheel.
A light beam *a* travels to the mirror
and returns as *b*. The beam is then
seen or not seen as *c*, depending on
whether it misses or hits a cog.

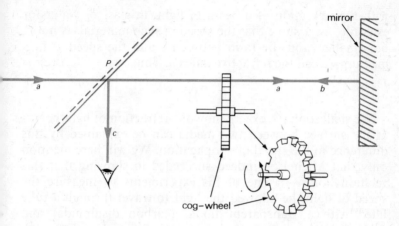

Figure 10. Foucault's principle of
measurement. The cube turns slightly
during the motion of the light so that
a ray emitted at *A* is reflected to *B*.

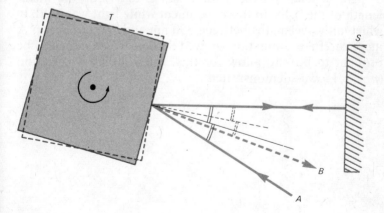

with the refraction of a beam of light, in glass or water for example, we assume that the speed in such materials is not c, but smaller, and the ratio between c and the speed V in a medium we call the refractive index n. Thus,

$$n = \frac{c}{V}$$

We shall soon see exactly how the refraction of light beams at the surface between two media can be explained by this difference in the speed of propagation. We will here mention only that Michelson indeed succeeded in showing that this relation holds. In one of his experiments to measure the speed of light, he allowed the light to travel through a tube filled with a transparent liquid (carbon disulphide) and noticed that the light took that much longer to travel through the tube, as was compatible with a speed equal to c/n, where n is the refractive index for carbon disulphide, which had been determined previously by other means. There was a complication because in any medium other than the vacuum the speed of light depends on the colour, that is to say on the wavelength of the light. In this experiment white light was used, in which all wavelengths between 390 nm and 760 nm occur. A more careful examination showed that a correction had to be brought to bear to allow for this, when the above relation ($n = c/V$) was demonstrated.

2 Refraction and reflection

10 Refraction at a boundary

When we try to catch a fish in an aquarium with our hands while looking in from above, we may sometimes miss it: the fish was not where we thought we saw it. Or, in other words, the light rays which reach us from a point in the water have had their direction of travel altered at some point; they have been refracted (figure 11). Where does this refraction take place? It is obvious that it must occur at the interface between water and air; there is, after all, no reason for a change in direction of the light beam in a homogeneous medium.

By linking the wave theory, in particular Huygens' principle, with Michelson's observations concerning the speed of light in matter, we can understand how refraction occurs at the interface between two media. For this purpose we look at figure 12. According to Huygens, we can think of the wavefront $A'\,B'$ as being originated by the emission of secondary wavelets out of each part of the wavefront AB. We have drawn one of the secondary wavelets, the one which emanated from A and reached A'. We can, however, turn the picture round and think of the wavefront AB as formed from $A'B'$ in the same way. For the latter case we have drawn the secondary wavelet emanating from B' and reaching B. The wave takes the same time to cover the distances AA' and BB'. Thus the ratio of the length AA' to BB' is the same as the ratio of the velocity of light in water (V') to that in air (V). Expressed mathematically,

$$\frac{AA'}{BB'} = \frac{V'}{V}.$$

In trigonometry the sine of an angle is defined as the ratio of the opposite side to the hypotenuse of a right-angled

30

2 Refraction and
reflection

Figure 11. How we see a fish in a pond.

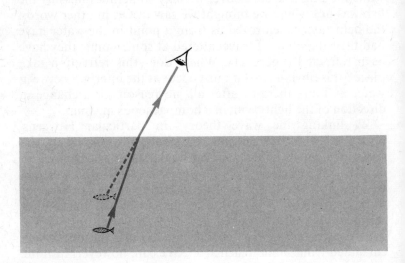

triangle. Using this definition for the angles i and i', which are respectively the angles made with the interface by the incoming and refracted wavefronts we can write

$$\frac{\text{sine } i'}{\text{sine } i} \equiv \frac{AA'/AB'}{BB'/AB'} = \frac{AA'}{BB'} = \frac{V'}{V}.$$

($\equiv$ means 'by definition equal to').
Going over to refractive indices, defined as

$$n = \frac{c}{V}, \quad n' = \frac{c}{V''},$$

Figure 12. Refraction explained by Huygens' principle.

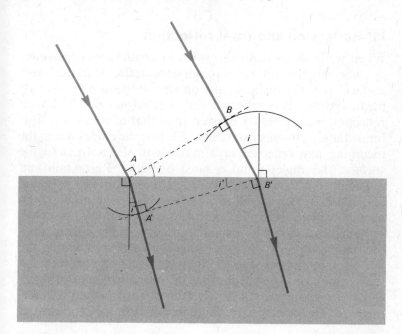

we obtain $\dfrac{\sin i'}{\sin i} = \dfrac{n}{n'}$ or $n' \sin i' = n \sin i$.

When written in the last formulation this relationship is known as Snell's law of refraction.

This law was originally enunciated for light rays. We know, however, that these are always perpendicular to the wavefronts and we can use the law in the same form, provided we remember that i' and i are the angles which the refracted ray makes with the normal to the surface (figure 12).

11 Reflection and total reflection

When we look into an overgrown aquarium from above we see, not only the fish, but also ourselves reflected in the water surface. If a ray of light falls on the interface between two media, part of it is reflected and part refracted. The law of reflection is more easily derived than that of refraction. It is immediately obvious from figure 13, that the angles which the incoming and reflected rays make with the normal to the surface, the angles i and r, must be equal. Refraction and reflection occur in such a way that the incoming, refracted and reflected rays all lie in a plane which also contains the normal to the surface. In figure 13 we have also drawn in the refracted ray. It makes a smaller angle with the normal than the incoming ray. We call this 'refraction towards the normal'. In the passage of light from air to water this is indeed the case. This means that the refractive index of water is greater than that of air: water is an 'optically denser' medium. The refractive index of air is almost the same as that of a vacuum, i.e. one ($n = \frac{c}{V}$, and in a vacuum $V = c$ hence $n_{\text{vacuum}} = 1$). The refractive index of water is about 1·3. The refractive indices of most kinds of glass lie between 1·4 and 1·8; diamond has a refractive index of 2·4.

We now perform the following thought-experiment at the boundary between two media: we allow the angle of incidence of a ray coming from the denser side (figure 14) to get larger and larger. The angle of refraction is in this case always larger than the angle of incidence (refraction away from the normal). At a particular angle of incidence i_c, the critical angle, the angle of refraction is 90°. It cannot get

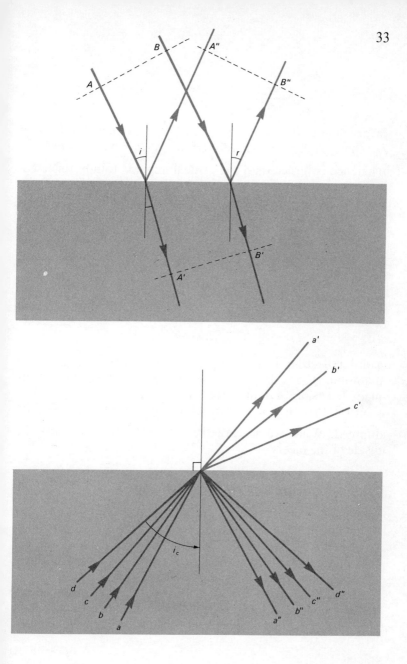

larger than that. If we increase the angle of incidence beyond i_c, there is no longer refraction. A ray whose angle of incidence is larger than the critical angle is totally reflected.

The magnitude of the critical angle is easily deduced from Snell's law:—$n' \sin i' = n \sin i$. Since the sine of 90° equals one, we have for i_c,

$$n \sin i_c = n'$$

If the less dense medium is air, then we can put n' equal to one and we get,

$$\sin i_c = \frac{1}{n}$$

Total reflection is responsible for the sparkling of a cut diamond. The light is reflected inside the diamond by the many facets, until it hits a facet with an angle of incidence less than i_c; then it comes out of the diamond, only slightly dimmed. What we see are the total reflections against the inside of the facets.

12 Applications of total reflection

The phenomenon of total reflection is often used in the optical trade: it is rather difficult to make loss-free mirrors in any other way. We would like to mention in passing some of the applications: they are beautiful examples of the usefulness of the theoretical developments we have just discussed.

The glass that is most often used for this purpose is a so-called crown glass (in particular boron silicate crown glass, a very transparent optical type of glass), whose refractive index is approximately 1·52. In the combination air-glass, i_c is, therefore, 41·1°. If a prism is made of this glass, as shown in figure 15, with angles 90°, 45° and 45° it can be used in a number of ways. In figure 16 the light beam is reflected through 90°. In figure 17 the light beam is reflected twice and simultaneously turned upside down: the beam coming in towards the right goes to the left after two reflections; furthermore the uppermost ray a in the incoming beam becomes the lowest ray a_1 in the reflected beam, and vice versa. A combination of two such prisms is shown in figure 18. With this one can interchange the upper and lower sides of a beam simultaneously with the interchange of the right and left sides. In binoculars use is made of positive lenses (which give a greater field of view than negative lenses). The images are then upside-down and also with left and right interchanged. By putting a set of these prisms in the viewer, the image can be put the right way round. Figure 19 shows a section through prism binoculars. The prism of figure 15 can be used in yet another way to interchange top and bottom of a beam (figure 20). In this case use is made of total reflection at the so-called hypotenuse surface AB. If such a prism is turned through an angle about the axis then the image is turned through double the angle.

13 Wavelength and colour

We have mentioned the colour of light and hinted that there is a connection between colour and wavelength. Let us now look a little more closely at this aspect of light, with reference to our previous discussion of refraction.

We imagine a glass prism P (figure 21) illuminated by a

Figures 15, 16 and 17. *Top* A prism
with angles 90°, 45° and 45°.
Middle Reflection through 90°.
Bottom Reflection through 180°.

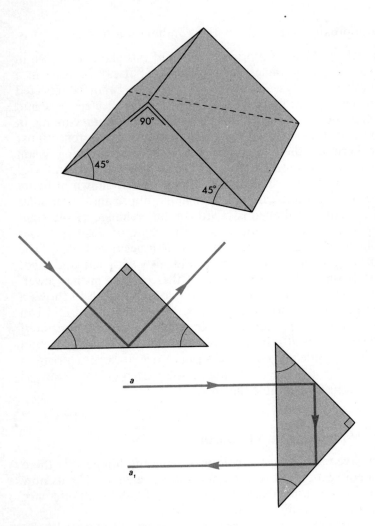

Figure 18. By combining two prisms,
left and right are interchanged;
so also are top and bottom.

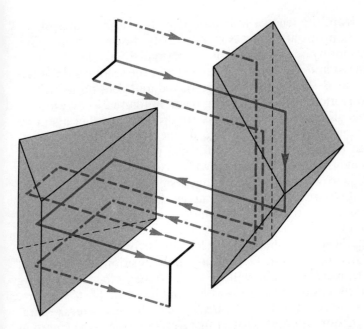

beam of white light. For us to be able to observe the phenomenon as clearly as possible the incoming light should be a
parallel beam. To obtain this we make use of a so-called
collimator, which is also shown in the figure, at C. A narrow
slit S is illuminated from the left. At L_1 there is a lens which
makes the beam emerging through the slit into a parallel
beam, provided S is at the focal point of L_1. (That this is the
right spot for the purpose is easily understood when it is
remembered that the path of the light beam is reversible. If
one thinks of a parallel beam coming from the right on to
this lens L_1, it will be focused at the focal point.)
The parallel beam which in our experiment moves to the

right from the lens L_1 falls on one of the sides of the prism. What happens after that is mostly easily shown by examining more closely one ray from the beam (figure 22). At A the ray is refracted and this refracted ray reaches the second side of the prism at B. There it is again refracted and goes on its way in the direction a'. The outgoing beam in figure 21 corresponds to this direction. Now the rays are brought together again by a second lens L_2. The image of the slit S is formed at T. When this experiment is performed it is found that there is not one image formed but a whole row of adjoining images. In this row the colour changes smoothly from red at R through red, orange, yellow, green, blue to violet at V. The row is called the spectrum, and its colours are the spectral colours.

At the place where the spectrum is formed we now put another narrow slit. Depending on its position, the colour of the transmitted light will be red, orange, etc. Anticipating later discussions, we can say here that it is possible to measure the wavelength of light. If this is done for the colours separated in our apparatus, it transpires that the wavelength is largest for red and smallest for violet light.

In table 1 we have gathered a few wavelengths in nanometer units.

For each wavelength the path of the beam in the prism is different and there is a different refractive index. This is in agreement with the results of Michelson's experiments, in which he found a relationship between the speed of light in a medium and the colour of the light. For the refractive index n is related to the velocity V by the equation $n = c/V$. One cannot, therefore, say that the refractive index of this glass is so much, but one can state its value for a number of wavelengths.

Table 1 Wavelengths

Red	780/630 **nm**
Orange	630/600
Yellow	600/570
Greenish yellow	570/550
Green	550/520
Blueish/green	520/500
Blue	500/450
Violet	450/380

To measure the refractive index one uses a goniometer. By determining the magnitude of the angle between the two sides of the prism (angle a in figure 22), and by measuring the angle of incidence on to the first face and the angle of refraction at the second, one can obtain the value of n by simple calculations.

The separation of wavelengths with a slit in the spectrum can be omitted in practical measurements. There are light sources which do not emit light containing all wavelengths but which on the contrary emit only a few wavelengths (i.e. which do not give a continuous spectrum). In their spectrum one therefore sees only a few lines. The above-mentioned measurements can then be carried out by looking at just one of these so-called spectral lines. For example the sodium lamp gives two closely spaced lines in the yellow and a few other much weaker lines. A mercury lamp which, like the sodium lamp, is often used for street lighting, emits principally two

Figures 19, 20 and 21. *Below*
A cross-section through prism binoculars
showing the prism combination in
figure 18. *Top right* Another way of
interchanging top and bottom. *Bottom right*
Refraction of a parallel beam by a prism.

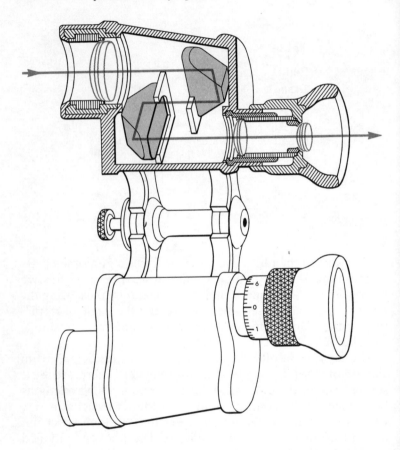

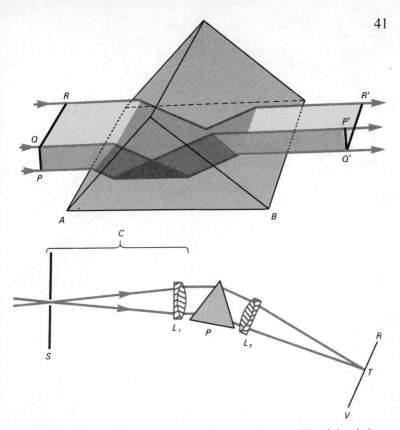

closely spaced yellow lines, one green line, a blueish-violet line and one line in the far violet, together with a few weaker lines in the red, blueish-green and violet parts of the spectrum.

These lamps are made to emit light by an electric discharge through a gas whose pressure is a few hundred atmospheres: sodium and mercury vapour respectively. They are called gas-discharge lamps. Other well-known gas discharge lamps are filled with neon or helium. Neon emits a score of lines in the red, and this red colour is well suited to attract attention in advertising signs. Of the many lines in the helium spectrum, the yellow is strongly predominant. By making mercury lamps out of blue glass the yellow lines are eliminated and

Figures 22 and 23. *Below* Newton's experiment
for the separation of colours with a prism.
Right Diagrams of a few spectra. Red is at
the top, violet at the bottom.

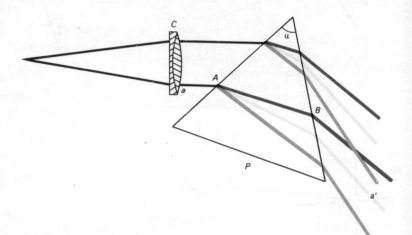

the green ones weakened; hence blue advertising signs.

The light from a normal mercury gas-discharge lamp
contains too little red emission to give agreeable lighting. By
mixing red light with mercury light the hue becomes whiter.
This can be achieved in the lamp itself by coating the inner
surface of the discharge tube with a thin layer of a substance
which fluoresces red light. What fluorescence means will be
considered later. The fluorescent lights now commonly used
everywhere are so provided, the fluorescence giving a continuous spectrum, mainly in the red.

Another gas-discharge lamp worth mentioning is the
hydrogen lamp. The hydrogen spectrum has red, blueish-
green and violet lines.

By using these and other spectral lines whose wavelengths
are accurately known, one can determine the refractive index
without the need of a slit in the spectrum.

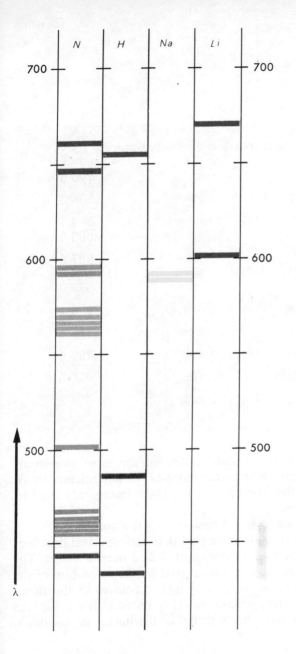

Table 2 Spectral lines and their wavelengths

b	Helium	He	Red	706·5 nm
C	Hydrogen	H	Red	656·3
D	Sodium	Na	Yellow	589·6
				589·0
d	Helium	He	Yellow	587·6
	Mercury	Hg	Yellow	579·1
				577·0
e	Mercury	Hg	Green	546·1
F	Hydrogen	H	Blueish/green	486·1
g	Mercury	Hg	Violet	435·8
G′	Hydrogen	H	Violet	435·0
L	Mercury	Hg	Violet	404·7

In table 2 we have listed a few of the most important spectral lines and their wavelengths (λ) in nanometers (nm). The letters in the first column are those commonly used to identify the lines.

In figure 23 we show schematically a few spectra.

On closer examination we find that each spectral line does not have precisely one wavelength, but a narrow range. The 'width' of this range depends in part on the resolution of the instrument, and also on the way light is emitted by the atoms in the light source. There are 'very narrow' lines, such as those for example emitted by a discharge in cadmium vapour. The lines of krypton are even narrower. One of the red lines of krypton is so sharp that all the light emitted has a wavelength between 605·7812 and 605·7800 nm, at least if the wavelength is measured in a vacuum. Light for which the spread in wavelengths is so small is called *monochromatic*, which literally means 'of one colour'. Even slightly broader spectral lines are called monochromatic.

We cannot here go into a detailed description of the methods used to measure wavelength, though we shall have a few words to say about that later. But it is interesting that the accuracy and the reproducibility of the measurement of the wavelength of the red krypton line has become so good that it has been adopted as a standard of length. The standard metre at Sèvres in France which, until recently, served as the unit of length, has been replaced by the following definition of the metre: the metre is 1650763·73 times the wavelength of a particular red krypton line when this is emitted unperturbed by the krypton atoms and measured in a vacuum.

One can express the fact that the refractive index of all materials varies with the wavelength by saying that all materials cause dispersion.

In general light sources also emit radiation with wavelengths outside the region of 380 to 780 nm. Because the human eye is only capable of perceiving radiation inside this region, the presence of the invisible radiation can be observed only indirectly.

The region with wavelengths shorter than 380 nm, that is shorter than the outermost visible violet, is called ultra-violet. The region where the wavelength is greater than the furthest red, i.e. larger than 780 nm, is called the infra-red. In a somewhat sloppy way one talks of ultra-violet and infra-red 'light'.

46

A rainbow in a painting by Rubens
(Wallace collection, London).

14 The Rainbow

Before moving on to other aspects of the refraction of light, we want to give a short description of a phenomenon known to everyone, which in all its colourful splendour never fails to fascinate the onlooker and for which the explanation is as surprising as it is old, but not, for all that, generally known. We refer to the rainbow. It can be seen when a rain cloud is lighted by the sun, or more precisely whenever any cloud with water droplets is so lighted. Thus rainbows can be seen close to waterfalls and even if, for example on the beach, one takes a shower in the sunshine.

We will have to examine what happens to light inside a droplet of water. Let us suppose that the raindrop is fairly precisely spherical in shape. Referring to figure 24 where the droplet is depicted, we imagine that sunlight shines on to it in a more or less parallel beam. The refractive index of water is about 4/3, that of the surrounding air 1. The ray of the incoming beam which goes through the centre of the sphere is marked a. Let us fix our attention on the ray b which is a given distance h from a.

The first time the surface of the sphere is met, the light ray is broken. The refracted ray reaches the far side of the sphere, and part of it is refracted out of the sphere. We are not interested in this twice refracted ray, but follow that part of the ray which is reflected at the second meeting with the sphere's surface. This ray moves inside the sphere until it reaches the surface for a third time. Here again part is reflected (of which more later) and part is refracted out of the sphere. In the figure the angle between the incoming ray b and the final outgoing ray b' is marked δ because this angle – the angle of deflection – is important in what follows.

If we look at the whole assembly of incoming rays, such as b,c,d (figure 24) then it will be apparent that the angle of deflection as a function of h first diminishes and then grows. There is, therefore, a particular value of h for which the angle of deflection is a minimum (ray c).

The rays coming in at the distance h corresponding to the minimum in δ and those incident with almost the same value of h will all leave the sphere in more or less the same direction. The other rays leave in many directions pointing further upwards (larger δ). There will, therefore, be more light in the direction corresponding to the minimum value of δ than upwards. In those directions where one is looking from above there is no light at all. A simple calculation shows that the minimum value of the angle of deflection δ is 42°.

Let us look at figure 25, a reproduction of an illustration from a book by Descartes published in 1637, in which an explanation of the rainbow was given for the first time. All the raindrops which, as seen by the observer E lie in a direction making 42° with the line ZM drawn through the sun and the observer direct their brightest rays towards E. They lie in a cone with ZM as axis and half angle at the apex of 42°.

Since the refractive index is different for different colours, the value of δ_{min} is different for each of them: for red 42°, for violet 40·5°. Because of this we get the beautifully coloured bow. The drops which lie inside the cone send some light towards E, those outside do not. The sky inside the rainbow is, therefore, brighter than outside.

In the same picture Descartes gives the explanation for the weaker rainbow which is nearly always visible together with the first. The second rainbow is produced by two internal reflections in the droplets. The half angle at the apex of the

Figures 24 and 25. *Below* A few light rays enter a raindrop and undergo successively refraction, reflection and another refraction. The ray *cc′* is least bent. The angle of minimum deviation is labelled δ min. *Right* The reproduction from Descartes' *Meteora* explains the rainbow.

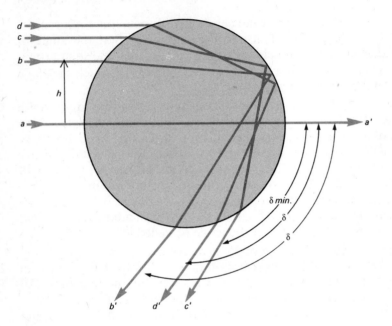

cone in which it is visible is approximately 51°. The red is now on the inside. The sky is therefore lighter on the inside of the bow.

More complicated, but even more beautiful, phenomena are seen when the droplets are illuminated with mono-chromatic light rather than with white light, and with a beam more nearly parallel than are sunbeams. The sun's diameter subtends an angle of about half a degree at the earth and the resultant spread in the inclination of the incoming light wipes out the finer details of the phenomenon.

In experiments with parallel beams of monochromatic

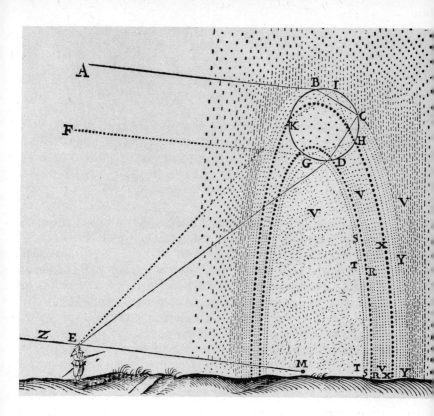

light in which the raindrops are replaced by glass balls, a
diffraction phenomenon occurs which splits the bow into a
large number of sharply defined lighter and darker bows.
It would take us too far afield to go into these interesting
curiosities in any fuller detail, and we must leave the phenomenon with this brief mention. We can just add that even
with sunlight something like it can sometimes be seen. When
the raindrops are very small, a fraction of a millimetre
across, then some so-called super-numerary rainbows can
be observed on the violet side of the main bow. They find
their origin in the above-mentioned diffraction effects.

One could go on a lot longer on this fascinating topic, but we must leave it here, simply restating that the light of the rainbow is reflected light whose source is the sun.

15 Lenses

In the experiment discussed in Section 13, we used lenses to give the wavefront the desired shape. The way a lens works is also dependent on the refraction of light at the interface between air and glass. Here also we have the choice of describing the properties of a lens in terms of wavefronts or light rays. In section 10 we discovered that Snell's law, $n' \sin i' = n \sin i$, is valid for both wavefronts and light rays. But there we considered only plane waves. In the case of a collimator lens (figure 26) whose purpose is to transform the spherical wavefronts emanating from a point source into a plane wavefront, it is very difficult mathematically to describe its working in terms of wavefronts. For precise calculations, which also must not be too extensive, the optical physicist prefers to work with light rays. There are rules and schemes which allow one to calculate exactly the path of a light ray through one or more lenses. We will not occupy ourselves with such things in this book, because they are not important in understanding the properties of light.

To obtain an insight into the mechanism of lens action, it is best to use wavefronts. We see in figure 26 that for this lens, which is convex (thicker in the middle than at the edges), the wavefront in the middle is slowed down (the light travels more slowly in the lens than in the surrounding air), so that the curvature of the front is diminished. This can even go so far (see figure 27) that the outgoing wavefront has the opposite curvature. If the lens is shaped so that the outgoing

Figures 26, 27 and 28. *Top* A collimator lens transforms a convex wavefront into a plane wave. *Middle* The transformation of a convex into a concave wavefront. *Bottom* A negative lens makes convex wavefronts more convex.

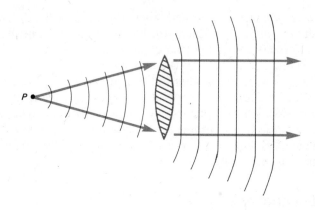

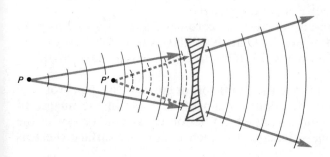

Figure 29. A cross-section of a beam in the presence of aberration.

wavefront is exactly spherical, then the light will all come together in a point which we call the image of the point from which the front emanated (the object). We then have a 'real image' of the point P at P'; the lens has a positive power. If we use a lens which is thinner in the middle than at the edges (a concave lens) then the curvature is changed the other way (see figure 28). It now appears as if the wavefronts leaving the lens have come from a point P'. This point is likewise called the image of P, but now it is a 'virtual' image. The lens used to obtain this has a negative power.

16 Spherical aberration

The formation of images by lenses throws up a lot of complicated problems. We already know that rays of different wavelengths are refracted differently at an interface. With lenses this leads to the conclusion that the formation of an image depends on the colour of the light. In figures 27 and 28 this would result in the point P' being at a different place for red light than for blue. This unfortunate side effect, which is related to the rainbow of section 14, is called chromatic aberration. By using a mirror instead of a lens, one is at once rid of it, for on reflection we always had $i = r$ (figure 13). independently of the wavelength.

One can also correct for chromatic aberration by making a lens out of two parts made of glasses whose dispersion (i.e. the relation between refractive index and wavelength) is different.

But even if one uses a mirror, or corrects for the chromatic aberration, there still remain other faults in the image. In figures 27 and 28, the object lies on the symmetry axis of the lens. If one calculates for such a case the surface the lens

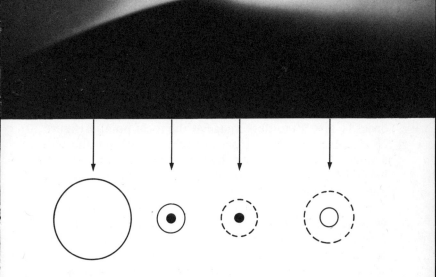

must have to produce purely spherical wavefronts on the image side (always to the right in our drawings), then the result is that the surface must be aspherical. That is to say: the surfaces of the lens must deviate from the spherical. That is a bothersome requirement because, technically, only the spherical shape can be made accurately without very great effort. The surfaces of lenses must be made to very small tolerances: they must not deviate from their prescribed shape by more than a fraction of the wavelength of the light that is to be used, otherwise there will be serious faults in the image formation, due to diffraction effects.

For an object on its axis, a lens with spherical surfaces exhibits spherical aberration, that is to say that the wave-fronts emitted by the point object on the axis do not converge exactly at one point image. Light rays which go through the outermost edge of the lens come together at a different spot from those which travel through the middle.

The result is that if a screen is placed at the expected point image, one does not see a point of light, but rather a circular spot with possibly rings around it (figure 29).

We consider now what shape a hollow mirror must have in order to give a faultless image at the focal point F (figure 30) of the distant object (for example a star) on the axis of symmetry. In such a case the wavefronts are spheres with so large a radius that we can regard them as plane waves in the region of the mirror. The number of crests and troughs between the position AA before the reflection and the convergence at F must be the same for each point in the wavefront, that is along each ray APF. Thus $(AP + PF)$ is a constant for all light rays. From the geometry of conical sections, we know, therefore, that the cross section of the mirror in the plane of the paper must be a parabola. The surface which is formed by rotating this curve about the axis of symmetry is called a *paraboloid*.

17 Object off the axis

It is therefore possible to produce an image without spherical aberration of an infinitely distant object, by using a parabolic mirror. If the object lies closer, then one has once again to worry about spherical aberration.

If the object is a long way off, but not on the axis, then again the parabolic mirror will not make a perfectly spherical

Figures 30 and 31. *Top* A parabolic mirror with the object some distance away on the axis. *Bottom* A parabolic mirror with the object to one side of the axis.

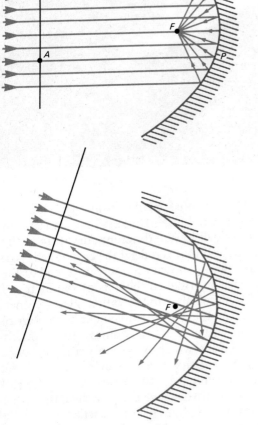

wavefront out of the incoming plane front. The lack of symmetry of the situation in figure 31 makes one suspect that the reflected wavefronts will have a different curvature at the bottom than at the top; and that is indeed the case. The image of an infinitely distant point, shown on a screen placed at the focal point of the mirror, normal to the axis of symmetry of the paraboloid, has a shape that looks rather like a comet, and is called *coma* (figure 32). This inconvenient behaviour of the parabolic mirror restricts its usefulness to infinitely distant objects in directions which make only a small angle with the axis; one says that the field of view is limited. One also has a similar inconvenience with lenses: a point object off the axis will in general always give rise to a deviation from spherical wavefronts on the image side of the lens.

Figure 32. The appearance of the coma
when the reflected rays in figure 31 are
shone perpendicularly on to a screen.

59

And even if we neglect the deviation from spherical shape
of the wavefronts, then we still observe that point objects
which lie in a plane produce images which do not. In other
words: a flat spot in the object space becomes bent in the
image space. In this way a three dimensional figure is always
distorted by a lens or a mirror.

By using several lenses in a row, in such a way that they
compensate for each other's errors as much as possible, it is
possible to make an image of a particular area, with only a
few small aberrations. Here begins the singular field of the
design of optical systems. This complicated work demands
not only a thorough knowledge of mathematics and optics,
but also a certain artistic insight. The many difficult calculations are nowadays mostly carried out on an electronic
computer. The conceiving of a set-up which satisfies certain
requirements will always remain most creative work.

18 Airy's disc

One can generally limit the aberrations of a lens by using
only the central portion of its surface. The smaller piece of
the wavefront that then reaches the image side will generally
more closely approach a spherical shape. One can achieve
this objective by grinding away the outer edge of the lens, but
also simply by putting in front of it a screen with a hole, a
diaphragm (figure 33). Unfortunately, the image now becomes less bright; the lens transmits a smaller fraction of the
spherical wavefront emitted by the object.

But if we take greater care, it becomes apparent that this
solution also is not complete. If we make the diaphragm
smaller and smaller, then to our amazement we see that the
image spot becomes larger again. Careful study shows that

Figures 33, 34 and 35. *Top* A lens with a diaphragm. *Bottom* A parallel beam of light falls on a screen with a narrow slit. *Right* Airy's diffraction pattern.

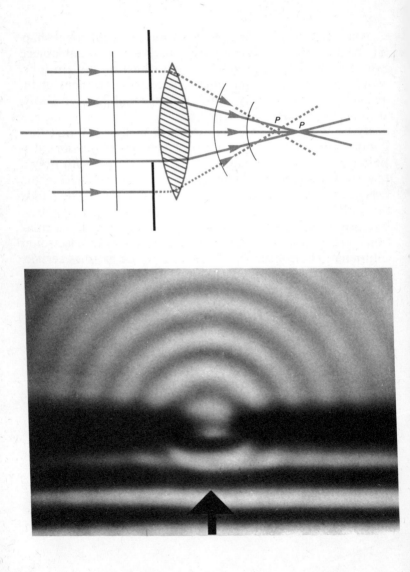

there is a disc surrounded by weaker concentric rings, which is called *Airy's disc*, after its discoverer. This image is similar to the already familiar image with spherical aberrations (see figure 29), but is more regular.

We now notice that a light beam cannot indefinitely be made thinner and thinner. The following experiment will show that the phenomenon of Airy's disc is indeed caused by the bounding of the light beams. We allow a wide parallel beam of light to fall on a screen with a small hole (figure 34). A good way off we put a second screen on which we observe Airy's disc, the diameter of which is seen to be inversely proportional to the diameter of the hole (and proportional to the wavelength of the light used). In figure 35, we show a photograph of Airy's disc, or diffraction pattern.

We will be able to explain this so-called diffraction phenomenon when we have studied the effects which appear as a result of the interference between several waves – a subject which we shall now broach.

3 Interference

19 Two sources and interference

In the previous sections we have seen what happens to a wavefront emanating in principle from a single light source, upon refraction and reflection: we have studied the transformations of such a wavefront by lenses and mirrors. Now we ask ourselves: what happens when two or more wave systems interact? At first sight it seems easy to predict what would be seen on such occasions.

If light falls on a screen S (figure 36) from two lamps L_1 and L_2 then the lighting is simply the sum of the lighting from the lamps when shining separately. A small rod P, placed some distance from S throws a shadow A at a spot reached by the light from L_2 but not by that from L_1 and another shadow B where only light from L_1 can come. Everywhere else we have the sum of the two illuminations. The more light sources, the better the lighting.

What can we conclude from that? Let us return to the waterwave model. We make circular ripples in the water with two small floats. We see that the two sets of circles travel right through one another. The displacement at any given point is the sum of the displacements caused by the two wave systems separately. If we now repeat the experiment, taking care to move the floats up and down together (more precisely, with the same oscillation frequency), then a remarkable phenomenon becomes visible in the whole area of the ripples (figure 37). There are regions where the ripples are present and others where no motion is visible.

Even this is understandable, after some further thought. We imagine the two floats to be at the points D_1 and D_2 of figure 38, and ask ourselves whether there are points such as P for which the difference between the distances PD_1 and

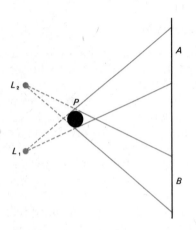

Figure 36. Illumination of a screen by two lamps. The obstacle P throws shadows at A and B.

PD_2 takes on a given value. A geometrical examination of the problem shows us that all the points P for which this difference equals a given distance e, lie on a pair of curves. Such a curve joining all the points with a common property, is called the locus of the point P. In this instance the locus is a hyperbola. Let e equal an integral number m times the wavelength, plus half a wavelength. Then each crest of the wave emanating from D_1 will reach a point P on the locus at the same time as the trough of the wave from D_2. They will cancel each other out exactly, and the point P will remain at rest. This is also what happens at every other point on the locus. All the points on the hyperbola remain at rest. The same thing will happen for the other 'half' of the hyperbola, for which the difference is $-e$. There will also be other such lines for different values of m. If on the other hand we take the value of e to be an integral number m times the wave-

Figures 37 and 38. *Top* The wave pattern formed by
two floats bobbing at the same frequency.
Bottom The curves join points of equal displacement.

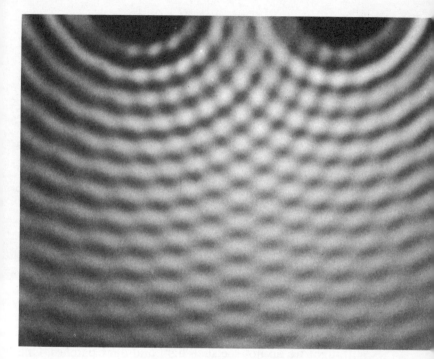

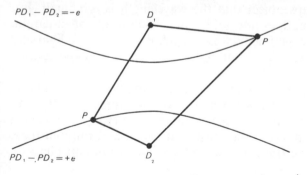

length, then the displacement at that point is twice that for each wave taken separately.

With light we do not see such light and dark patches. One might perhaps object that the wavelength is too small. But this objection does not hold water. Even in the most careful and refined experiments it is not possible to observe light and dark patches, at any rate as long as one uses two separate light sources.

Let us repeat the experiment with the water in a slightly different way. We set the source of vibrations D_1 into oscillation, but after it has been allowed to radiate for a short time, we stop it and then restart it again, at a random time, with the same frequency as before, but in random phase to

Figure 39. The wave pattern
formed by two floats bobbing
at different frequencies.
The hyperbolas are washed out.

the previous oscillations. We do the same thing with the source D_2 but independently from D_1. We then see a disturbance on the water surface, but without any regular pattern; see figure 39. If we had stopped and started D_1 and D_2 together each time, then every train of waves from D_1 would still have met the corresponding group from D_2 and the pattern of 'light and dark' regions would have been the same as in figure 37. The length of each train depends on how long D_1 and D_2 remain unperturbed while radiating. Such a train could contain ten or thirty waves.

It might, therefore, be that something similar to the above takes place in the case of light. A light source consists of many independent small sources, which emit light waves during some time peculiar to each one of them and then do nothing more. The light sent out by the whole source is a mixture of the light emitted by each of the independent smaller light sources and this is quite a random unsystematic affair. Since for the two light sources which we considered earlier the motion of the internal light sources are quite independent, we can hardly expect to obtain a regular pattern of light and dark on the screen.

Only if each little jump, every beginning and every end of emission coincided precisely in the sources L_1 and L_2 could there appear a steady pattern of light and dark instead of the even lighting of the screen. Light sources having such a property would be called *coherent*. The sources in figure 36 are incoherent.

It is indeed remarkable that it has proved possible to make coherent light sources. The patterns obtained with them are beautiful and the interactions which give rise to them have been labelled interference. We shall now say a thing or two about this fascinating subject.

In order to make the connection with what has gone before we first mention that an atom emitting light only does so for about 10^{-9} seconds, i.e. about one thousand-millionth of a second. Since the speed of light is about three hundred million metres per second, it follows that the train of waves is about thirty centimetres long. This length is equal to about fifty thousand times the wavelength: the length of the train is about 50,000 wavelengths.

If it were possible to measure the intensity of the light reaching the screen S in figure 36 within a thousand-millionth of a second, we would observe very sharp changes in the brightness of the light. Luckily our eyes are much too slow to see such rapid changes. Changes of about thirty times a second can just about be seen, but faster ones certainly cannot. The result is that what we see as a quite constant brightness is in fact changing sharply in shots of one thousand-millionth of a second each.

20 How to obtain coherent light sources

Of the different ways of making (mutually) coherent light sources, we will mention just two. They were both discovered at the beginning of the nineteenth century and are linked with the names of Fresnel and Thomas Young.

Let us consider the screen S (figure 40) with two narrow slits O_1 and O_2 illuminated from the left. After going through the slits the light will not only travel straight on, but it will also be diffracted sideways. The point P will, therefore, get light from both O_1 and O_2. Since, unless further precautions are taken, these two slits (considered as light sources) are not coherent, the superposition on to a screen T of the light emitted from them would only give an even lighting. Matters become drastically different if the light is made to pass through a small pinhole O (figure 41) before it reaches the screen S with the slits. For from O light waves travel towards the right until at a certain time the wavefront F reaches the screen S. Parts of this wavefront go through the slits O_1 and O_2 and the light coming from the slits now has the special property that it all comes from the same wavefront F. Every arbitrary change in the emission of light from O will, after reaching S, affect the light from O_1 and O_2 in like manner. In other words, the light travelling to the right from O_1 and O_2 is coherent.

And look: there really do appear light and dark patches on the screen! If one chooses to make the openings O_1 and O_2 in the shape of slits (at right angles to the plane of the drawing in figure 41), then the interference pattern shows itself as a row of light and darker lines or fringes. If the slits are close together, then the light falling upon them is already nearly coherent. If they are further apart then the coherence producing slit O must be made narrow and placed some distance away from the double slit.

It is also possible to produce two coherent light sources in a different way (Fresnel). Light which has passed through a narrow slit O (see figure 42) falls on two mirrors M_1 and M_2. The light beams reflected by the mirrors behave as if they had come from the point O'_1 and O'_2. These points are the images formed by the mirrors. They are not 'real' but 'virtual' images. For them it is again true that each change in emission of one is exactly paralleled by a change in emission of the other, since the light of both has originated from the same real source O. Once again the interference patterns make their appearance.

If O is in the shape of a slit perpendicular to the plane of

Figures 40, 41 and 42. *Top* Incoherent illumination of two slits. The light source L is large, seen from the slits O_1 and O_2 in the screen S. The screen T is evenly illuminated, without the appearance of equally spaced fringes. *Bottom* Coherent illumination of two slits. The light source is now made small by the slit O. O_1 and O_2 are illuminated by the same wave. Equally spaced fringes appear on T; for example, there is a dark fringe at P. The intensity of the light, I, is shown to the right of T.
Right Fresnel's mirror experiment, in which two coherent light sources, O_1' and O_2' are made from one incoherent source, O.

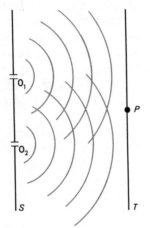

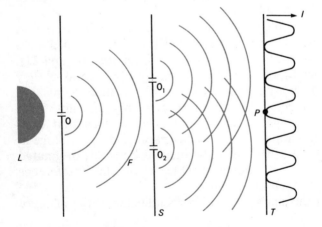

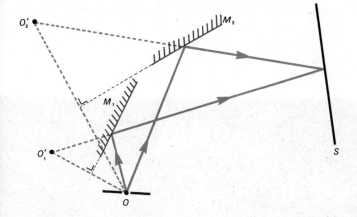

the drawing in figure 42, then screen T shows light and dark fringes. This also happens when, as in figure 41, O as well as O_1 and O_2 are slits perpendicular to the drawing. The use of slits gives a brighter image than the use of small holes. By measuring the distance between the fringes of the interference pattern, it is possible to calculate the wavelength of the light used in the experiment.

If in figure 41, we call the distance between the slits O_1 and O_2 h, and the distance between the screens S and T l, then a simple calculation of the difference in path length from O_1 and O_2 to the bright and dark lines on T shows that the distance d between fringes must be equal to $\frac{l\lambda}{h}$, i.e.,

$$\lambda = \frac{hd}{l}$$

If the experiment is done with monochromatic light, then one can indeed obtain the value of λ but unfortunately the sharpness of the fringes is then very poor. Light and dark go into each other smoothly, and this method does not, therefore, allow one to make accurate measurements of wavelength. Luckily there are, as we shall see later, other more accurate ways of doing this.

The diffraction pattern from five equal slits,
each 1μ wide, equidistant from each other by 5 mm.

Figure 43. Positions of maxima and
minima for various wavelengths.

If white light is used, the interference pattern looks rather different. White light contains all the different wavelengths in the visible spectrum, for each of which the maxima and minima will fall at a different place.

We shall examine this in more detail for a special case, with the help of figure 43. Let the dimensions be such that for red light of wavelength 600 nm, the maxima lie 4 mm apart. The minima lie between them, also a distance of 4 mm apart. From the middle of the pattern where there is a maximum, we therefore get a maximum for this wavelength every 4 mm. This is represented graphically in the second line of figure 43. Above that is the representation of the pattern for light of 700 nm wavelength, below that for 500 and 400 nm. At A only the pattern for 700 nm has a maximum. At B the 600 nm pattern has a maximum, the one for 400 nm a minimum. Yet the light seen there is not that corresponding to 600 nm (red) because many other wavelengths throw some light at the same place. The colour actually observed is a whitish pink.

On the left side of the pattern the same order of colours is symmetrically repeated: white (at P), yellow brown, pink, violet . . . . One does not therefore see many fringes in white light.

21 The doubling of wavefronts

Yet another way of making coherent light sources rests on the possibility of partially reflecting a wavefront and of mixing the reflected beam and the transmitted beams at a later stage. In figure 44, D represents a mirror covered on one side by a thin layer of metal (aluminium for instance) so that, of the light falling upon it, half is transmitted and half is reflected. It is a so-called semi-transparent mirror. Such a

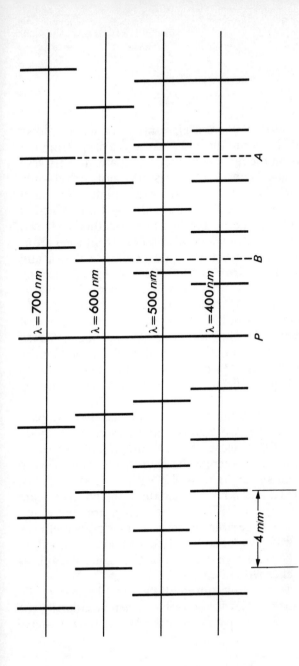

mirror must be supported on a glass plate. In what follows we shall completely ignore the complications arising from the weak reflections on the far side of the glass plate, and also the fact that the light beams of interest do not travel only through air but also through this glass plate. We shall proceed as if we were dealing just with the thin reflecting surface of the metal. The mirror is set up together with two other mirrors M_1 and M_2 which also reflect from their front surface. All these mirrors must be particularly smooth and flat. The light comes in from the left. Part of it is let through by D. The transmitted beam strikes M_1, is reflected towards D, striking D from the right, and again half is transmitted to the left (that part is not of interest to us), while the other half is reflected downwards. Half the original beam was reflected upwards by D (this beam is shown dotted in the figure). After reflection by M_2 this part is also split by D into an (uninteresting) beam reflected to the left and the beam b, transmitted downwards.

By following a ray in the beam, we can see that the path difference between the two beams a and b is equal to twice the distance $PA - PB$, at least when M_1 and M_2 are perpendicular to each other (as shown in the figure), and when D is so oriented that it makes an angle of 45° with both M_1 and M_2.

The two beams a and b both originate in the parallel beam falling on to the system from the left. They are, therefore, coherent and we will be able to observe interference effects. The apparatus was developed by Michelson and is called an *interferometer*, because one can measure distance as well as observe interference with it.

To see this let us follow more closely a few light rays. To make things a little easier for ourselves when comparing the paths after the splittings by D, we draw in the mirror image

M'_1 of M_1 formed by D. The length of the line AR drawn from a point A on D to R on M_1 is equal to that of AR' (see figure 45). In figure 45, it is assumed that the mirrors are set up such that M'_1 makes a small angle with M_2 and that they bisect each other at P. The light paths a_1 and a_2 of the rays through P are then equal. The rays b_1 and b_2, however, have different path lengths, the difference being twice QR'.

If we look from O into the interferometer and use monochromatic light, we will see a series of light and dark fringes. At P the light intensity is strongest (equal path lengths) and other maxima appear whenever $2QR'$ equals a whole number of wavelengths of the light. Between them there are the minima, where $2QR'$ equals a whole number of wavelengths, plus half a wavelength.

To make measurements of distance, M_2 is mounted on a slide which can be moved very smoothly backwards and forwards by a screw mechanism, in the direction QA. A mark is made in the viewing field, let us suppose at P. By screwing M_2 further away, the path difference at P is changed from its previous value of zero. A movement l causes a path difference $2l$. All parts of the field of view have received this same path difference. Therefore, when M_2 is screwed back one sees the fringes moving from right to left. In principle it is possible to compare in this way each movement of M_2 with the wavelength of the light used in the experiment, or conversely, to obtain the wavelength by measuring the movement of M_2 needed to cause a given number of fringes to cross the mark. Each fringe which crosses implies a movement of M_2 through half a wavelength. Such measurements are, of course, possible but to measure for example a distance of 1 dm, or conversely, to compare the wavelength with a distance of 1 dm, one would have to count several hundred

Figure 44. An interferometer. The semi-transparent mirror D splits the incoming wavefront into two parts, which come together again at O via M_1 and M_2.

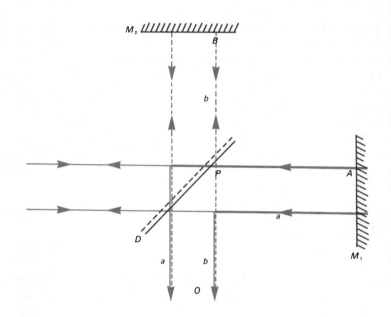

thousand fringes crossing the mark. Nobody can be expected to do this without making mistakes, and even if he could it would take him so long that temperature variations would ruin the accuracy of the result.

If shorter distances are measured then the accuracy falls off again. An error of 0·0002 mm in the distance of 1 dm means an accuracy of two millionths, but the same error in a distance of 1 mm, is but one five-thousandth.

But of course scientists have not rested until they found ways of accurately comparing the wavelengths of different spectral lines. We shall return to this later.

Figure 45. The mirrors M_1 and M_2
are not mutually perpendicular.

79

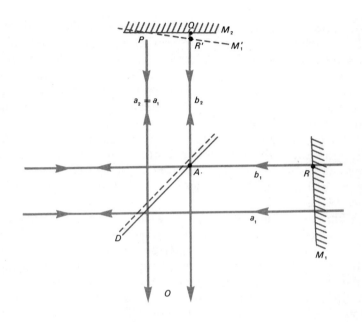

22 The star interferometer

In the meantime we want to discuss a few other experiments relating to interference. We first describe an experiment which anybody can do for himself. With a fine needle make two small round holes as close together as possible in a piece of black paper. In the evening hold the holes over one eye, close the other and look at a lamp a long way away, for example a fluorescent lamp or a sodium lamp more than a hundred yards away. The lamp plays the role of the slit in figure 41. The line joining the holes must lie across the length of lamp (figure 46). We now follow two parallel rays, one from each opening. These are brought together by the eye at its focal plane, the retina at the back of the eye which forms a light sensitive screen. Even parallel light beams coming from widely separated objects are brought together on to the retina of a normal eye; it makes a sharp image of the object. In one direction, so chosen that the rays have a path difference AB at the paper, equal (see figure 47) to a whole number of wavelengths, they will reinforce each other; in that direction the eye sees a maximum. The maxima are separated by minima, for which the path difference AB is an odd number of half-wavelengths.

This experiment is a charming and diverting demonstration, but can nevertheless be looked upon as a simplified version of another kind of interferometer. Imagine that we try to do the experiment with a lamp that is too close by, so that we can see the thickness of the fluorescent tube. Each strip of the tube then gives rise to an interference pattern, but those of different strips do not fall on top of each other: the complete pattern is weakened or may even be completely wiped out. This is equivalent to having too wide a slit in the experiment illustrated in figure 41. The light beams are no longer coherent.

This consideration led Michelson to a method which allowed him to measure the diameter of a star. We know already that a perfect telescope under perfect atmospheric conditions never sees more of a star than the Airy diffraction pattern (section 18). The origin of this disc is not to be ascribed to the star, but to the telescope.

Four mirrors were mounted on to a telescope, as shown in figure 48, and the whole was aimed at a star.

The distance between the holes in the black paper is

Figures 46 and 47. *Top* A simple
experiment on interference. *Bottom* Parallel
beams from the two slits.

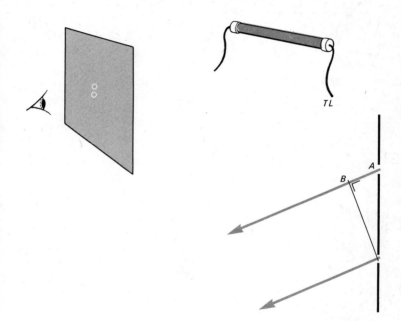

equivalent to the distance marked *a* in figure 48. The mirrors
M_1 and M_2 were placed on a beam and the distance between
them could be altered. When they were close together, all
stars produced interference fringes. For the star *a* of the
constellation Orion, known as Betelgeuse, it proved possible
to make the pattern disappear by increasing the distance M_1
M_2. From a knowledge of this critical distance, the diameter
of the star was calculated to be 0·047″ (47 thousandths of a
second of arc), an angle which is subtended by a distance of
1 mm, 4·4 km away. The disc of the star is just big enough to
cause the interference pattern to disappear for large distances

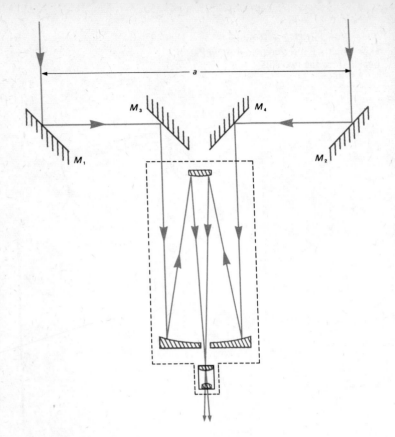

between the mirrors. This is the same effect as that of just-too-wide a slit in the experiment of figure 41, or with too wide a fluorescent tube in the experiment with the two holes in the black paper in front of the eye.

Such a star-interferometer cannot be made at home. The beam is 6·3 metres long and in later instruments has been lengthened to 15 m. The mirror of the telescope must also have a large diameter in order that there may be enough intensity, even after the great enlargement of the image, needed to separate the fine interference fringes. The experiment described above took place in California, using a mirror 2·5 m in diameter.

Figure 48. The star-interferometer. 83
The two incoming beams are brought
together with a telescope. Apart from
this, everything is similar to the
experiment depicted in figure 46.

23 Newton's rings

At this point we want to describe a completely different way
of causing interference patterns, a method which has been
widely used in practice. We refer to Newton's experiment
with thin layers of air between pieces of glass.

On a flat plate of glass P (figure 49) is placed a glass lens L,
of which the top surface is flat and the bottom very slightly
curved. Except at the contact point A of the two pieces of
glass, there is between them a layer of air, which is very thin
near A and becomes progressively thicker further out. Before
we describe the experiment itself, we want to say a few words
about the thickness of the layer of air.

The bottom profile of the lens is shown in the figure by a
circle of radius r. The thickness p of the air layer a distance
d from A is then to a good approximation equal to $d^2/2r$, as
can easily be shown mathematically.

Coming back to the experiment, we put a semi-transparent
mirror S obliquely above the lens and plate, so that the light
shining on to S is directed downwards on to the lens (see
figure 50). The eye of the observer is supposed to be at O,
some distance above the lens.

We pay no attention to the light reflected by the top
surface of the lens, but look at the beams which are reflected
by the curved side. The intensity of each of these is about 4
per cent of the incoming light, so that they are of about equal
intensity. At the point B in figure 49, the beam a is behind,
relative to b, by a distance equal to twice the thickness of the
layer of air at that point. If this thickness is half a wavelength,
then the difference in paths of the two beams is a whole
number of wavelengths. One would think at these points, the
two beams would reinforce one another.

Figures 49 and 50. *Left* A lens on a flat plate.
Right A method of observing Newton's rings.

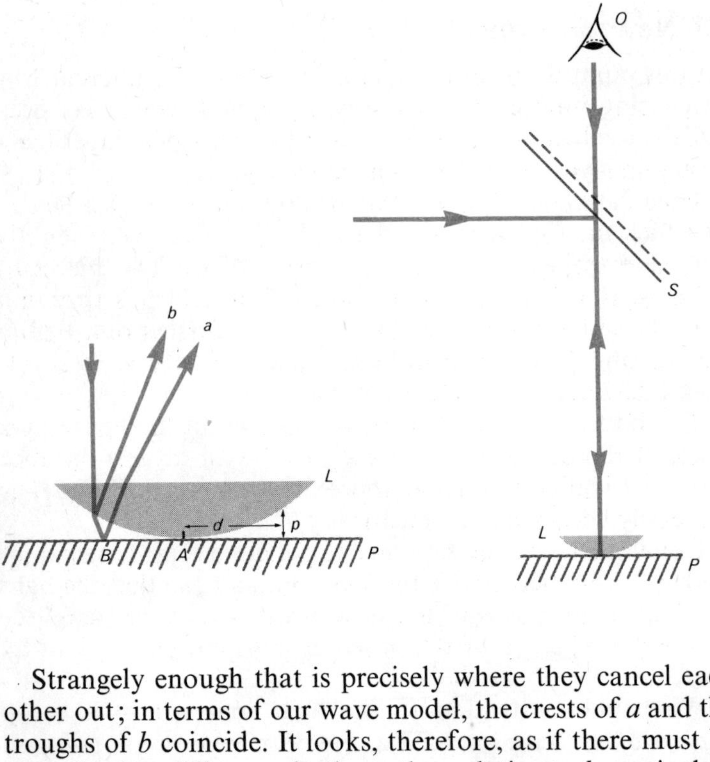

Strangely enough that is precisely where they cancel each other out; in terms of our wave model, the crests of *a* and the troughs of *b* coincide. It looks, therefore, as if there must be some further difference in the path *a* relative to *b*, equivalent to a further half-wavelength.

A theoretical analysis shows that this is indeed the case. Upon reflection of light from a denser medium (e.g. for light falling from air on to glass), the reflected lightwave travels as if it had fallen a half-wavelength behind. Upon reflection in a dense medium (e.g. glass) at an interface with a lighter medium (for example air) this phenomenon does not occur.

Apart from the jump in the phase, equivalent to the loss of half a wavelength, which in our case occurs only for the beam *a* reflected from the plate, the differences in path length due to the air layer must also be taken into account. Therefore, whenever twice the thickness *p* of the layer of air is an integral number of wavelengths, there is darkness. This is the case then for:

$$p = \tfrac{1}{2}\lambda, \tfrac{3}{2}\lambda, \tfrac{5}{2}\lambda \text{ etc.}$$

On the other hand, the beams reinforce each other when:—

$$p = \tfrac{1}{4}\lambda, \tfrac{3}{4}\lambda, \tfrac{5}{4}\lambda \text{ etc.}$$

In the middle, at the point of contact, there is no air and $p = 0$, which means darkness, since this value fits into the first series. This is after all to be expected: where glass goes smoothly over into glass, we do not expect any reflection of light at all. If we look, therefore, from above the lens, the point of contact *A* is dark. Where $p = \tfrac{1}{4}\lambda$ there is light and that is the case in a ring around *A*, with a radius *d* obeying the formula,

$$d^2/2r = \tfrac{1}{4}\lambda, \text{ or } d_1 = \sqrt{2r.\tfrac{1}{4}\lambda}$$

The second light ring occurs when

$$d_2 = \sqrt{\frac{2r.3\lambda}{4}}$$

A number of light rings will be visible, separated by dark ones. Substituting $\dfrac{4d^2}{2r\lambda} = q$, the radii of the light rings are obtained for $q = 1, 3, 5$, etc. and those of the dark rings for $q = 0, 2, 4$ and so on.

That is the explanation of the origin of 'Newton's rings'. If

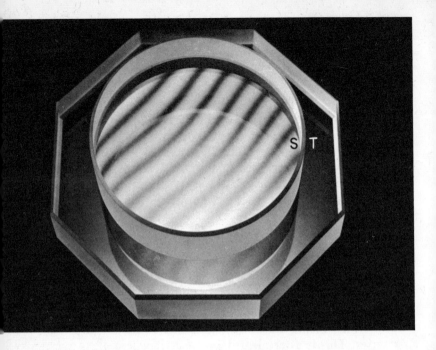

one measures the diameter of the rings, one can obtain the wavelength of the light, provided the radius of curvature of the lens is known from some other measurement. The converse is, however, of great importance to the optician and is used daily in his workshop.

Every flat, hollow or convex surface is made into the right shape by use of a testing glass. Before a surface can be worked on, the testing glass must first be prepared. Further, each hollow testing glass (used consequently to make convex lenses) has its own particular convex testing glass. The surfaces of all precision-made optics have, with a few exceptions such as parabolic mirrors, the shape of a concave or convex sphere; they are spherical (if they are not flat). Spherical and flat surfaces are the only ones that can match each other in all orientations. The sphericity and correct curvature of the surface being made is tested in a set-up such as the one

Figures 51 and 52. *Left* The testing of
a surface with a testing glass. *Below* Interface
of a thin film of oil on water.

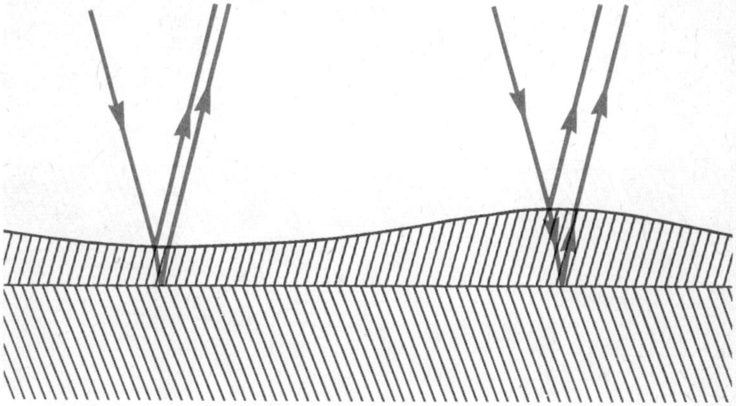

sketched in figure 50. If the match is not perfect, interference lines appear, which originate in the thin layers of air between the surface S to be tested and the testing glass T (figure 51).

24 Interference in thin layers

The patches of oil on water which sometimes cause such beautiful colours are thin layers from which light is reflected at the top and bottom surface, causing the colours by interference; see figure 52. Because the oil is not of uniform thickness, the colour changes from place to place. The colours of soap bubbles arise in the same way.

Practically every user of an optical instrument has heard that the purple tint of his camera lens or of the lenses on his binoculars, or of his spectacles, is caused by 'coating'. In

Figure 53. A thin film on glass.

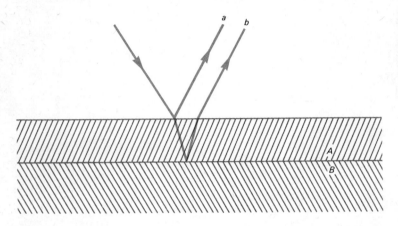

connection with the previous discussion we can now explain how this works and why coatings are used.

We examine to this end what happens if there is a layer A (figure 53) with refractive index n on a piece of glass B, whose refractive index is n', such that n is less than n'. The difference in the paths of the reflected beams is $2d$, where d is the thickness of the layer. For the beam a which comes from air (refractive index 1) on to A, there is a jump in phase equivalent to a loss of half a wavelength. The reflection at the interface between A and B also causes such a phase change, and we must, therefore, take as the path difference between a and b just the distance $2d$. There will, therefore, be an extinction where $2d$ equals a half a wavelength; to be precise the half of a wavelength in the medium A. The thickness is then one quarter wavelength. Such layers are called quarter-lambda layers; lambda is the name of the Greek letter λ which is always used to denote the wavelength of light.

For that wavelength, such that $d = \frac{1}{4}\lambda$, no light will be reflected, provided the beams a and b are of equal intensity. This is not generally the case. One can, however, find materials for which, when they are deposited on to glass in such a thin coating, the reflected light is less than one per cent of the total, if only for a given region of wavelengths.

The process of covering glass surfaces with such non-reflecting layers is called *coating*. The advantages are obvious. In a pair of binoculars for example (figure 19) there are ten glass-air surfaces. By reflections alone, about 40 per cent of the light would be lost, since one glass-air interface reflects 4 to 6 per cent of the light. By coating all the surfaces, this loss is reduced to 10 per cent.

There is another advantage, at least as important. The light reflected at the glass surface can, after subsequent reflections, go in the direction in which the image is formed (figure 54). The beams which reach either the film of the camera, or the eye of the observer after an even number of reflections do not, it is true, give rise to a sharp image, but they do form a haze over the direct image. They reduce the contrast. And the unpleasantness can take on quite serious aspects. The picture of a landscape can for example be fogged by the light of the sky above the landscape. The great expanse thereof causes a lot of stray light to reach the film; see figure 55. That is why one must not allow the sun to shine into the lens. The photograph in figure 55 is made with an uncoated lens.

The coating enhances the *brilliance* of the picture. From this discussion it will be clear that it is impossible to deal with the whole spectrum with one coating. If the $\frac{1}{4}\lambda$ layer is right for green light with $\lambda = 560$ nm, it is obviously not right for red light with $\lambda = 720$ nm, or for violet light with $\lambda = 400$ nm. Those parts of the spectrum are, therefore, reflected, and this causes the purple bloom of such layers in reflected light. Red and blue-violet together make purple.

By having more than one layer and by choosing the materials carefully, it is possible to obtain an important reduction of reflection over the whole visible spectrum.

A few words about the making of these layers, whose thickness is only about a thousandth of a millimeter. For one layer, magnesium fluoride is used. If more than one layer is needed, one can for example use alternately magnesium fluoride and zinc sulphide.

These substances are salts which melt and evaporate at high temperatures. They are placed in little boats of high melting-point metal, in a vacuum chamber, which is pumped down to one hundred-millionths (10^{-8}) of an atmosphere. In this chamber, suspended above the boats, are glass surfaces to be coated. The boats are heated electrically. The salt melts and evaporates. The vapour hits the glass and condenses. By measuring the reflection of light from one of the glass surfaces

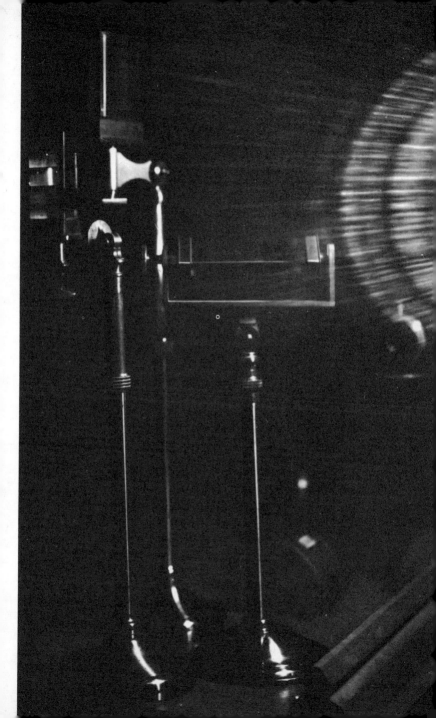

during the vacuum coating process, and pushing a screen (still in the vacuum) between the boats and the glass as soon as the reflection has become minimal, one can succeed in making $\frac{1}{4}\lambda$ layers. We will not go into the many technical processes needed to make good, well-sticking coatings. It has become an established technology.

25 The Fabry-Perot interferometer

Before leaving interferometers altogether, we want to pay attention to one more special kind, of which the theory and the practice have proved to be of great importance.

We imagine two flat glass plates set up parallel to one another (figure 56). The facing surfaces have been made flat with the utmost care (to one twenty-thousandth of a millimeter or better) and both of them have been provided with a mirror (by evaporation) which reflects 99 per cent and transmits one per cent of the light. From the left a parallel beam of light falls on these mirrors and it becomes important in the first place to understand what takes place in the space between the mirrors.

In the cases of interference which we have discussed up to now, we had to do with two interfering beams which could reinforce or weaken each other. Now, however, the set-up of the two good mirrors brings a new element into play: a great deal of the light energy travels back and forth between the mirrors; only a small part of it disappears from the space between them at each reflection. To be able to describe the consequences of this we have drawn in figure 56 a small part a of the beam which has come through the first mirror. This beam travels to the right, meets the second mirror and turns (b), only slightly weakened, back to the left, meets the first

Figure 56. The Fabry-Perot interferometer.   93
Waves are reflected backwards and forwards
between two mirrors.

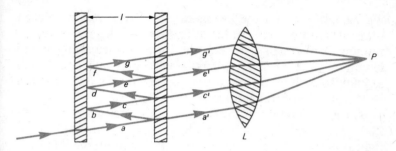

mirror, is thereby reflected to the right (c) again only slightly
weakened, and so on.

To make the course of events clearer, the beams have not
been drawn exactly across the mirrors, but at a slight angle to
the normal to the mirrors. In that way we see the beams
travelling next to each other. From a, a small fraction a' has
escaped through the second mirror, from c also a small part
c' and so on. Similarly, parts of b and the other beams
travelling to the left are lost to the outer space. These have
not been drawn in, because we shall concern ourselves only
with the beams a', c' etc.

Past the second mirror there is a lens system L which
focusses all the parallel beams at a point P on its focal plane.
The distance l is large compared to all the wavelengths of
visible light. The length $2l$ of a round trip of a beam will be
equal to exactly a whole number of wavelengths for some
particular wavelengths. Let us make that clear by an example.
If $l = 2$ cm, then $2l$ is exactly 80,000 times the wavelength
500 nm. But it is also exactly 80,001 times the wavelength
499·99375 nm and also precisely 80,002 times 499·9750 nm,
or 79,999 times 500·00625 nm and so on. Furthermore, $2l$
is then also 80,000·5 times 499·996875 nm. Thus for the

wavelength 500 nm the beams a' and c' will reinforce each other (because their path difference is exactly a whole number of wavelengths). For the rather closely lying wavelength of 499·996875 nm, a' and c' will practically completely extinguish each other, and e' and g' likewise. That wavelength is, therefore, not transmitted by the two plates.

By the interaction of the many beams, the two plates have become a highly selective wavelength filter. The transmitted light is not greatly weakened, for although it is true that only one per cent of a is transmitted in a', nevertheless there are many beams a', c', e' etc. which together add up to quite a bit of the light. The intensity of the beam c is (after two reflections) still $0·99 \times 0·99a$, so that c' is $0·01 \times 0·99 \times 0·99a$, while a' is $0·01a$. The extraordinary result is, therefore, that the interfering beams only slowly diminish in intensity.

The interferometer we have here described, the Fabry-Perot interferometer, is named after those who developed it. When the incoming beam is parallel (which can be achieved using a collimator lens), the path difference between the interfering beams (a' and c') is the same for all points in the beam. The amplitude of the transmitted beam is then constant at all points to the right of the second mirror. If the light comes from a point source, the path difference depends on the angle that the incoming ray makes with the surface of the mirrors.

From the symmetry of the situation, we expect a circular interference pattern whose centre should lie at the foot of the normal to the mirrors, drawn through the light source. We do indeed see such rings, and the spacing between them is a function of the wavelength of the light and the geometry of the apparatus (figure 57).

The more obliquely the beams travel, the sooner will they

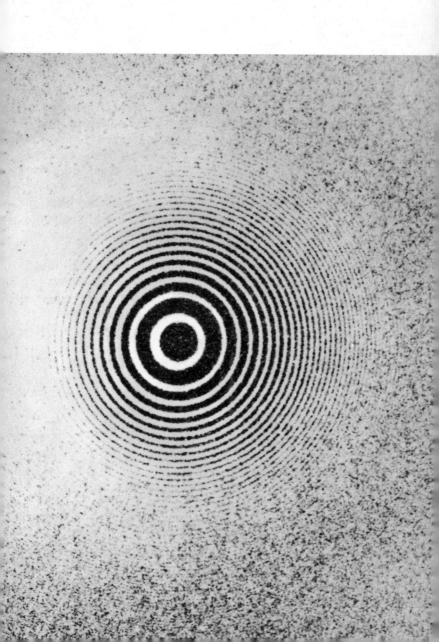

Figure 57. Interference rings produced by a Fabry-Perot interferometer.

come to the end of the mirrors on their back and forth motion, and the sooner therefore will they be lost to the formation of the rings. Although great numbers of beams such as a', c' etc. contribute to obtain the sharpness of the rings, the number remains finite, and will not easily exceed thirty, especially not if the distance l between the mirrors is large. Wavelength differences of one four hundred-thousandth of a wavelength can be detected with this instrument.

From this example it can be seen without further elaboration that this interferometer makes a sharp distinction between even closely lying wavelengths. It is, therefore, not surprising that the apparatus has served, and still does, for the comparison of wavelengths. With a few modifications it has even proved useful in the measurement of distances expressed in terms of the wavelength of a chosen spectral line.

4 Diffraction

26 Diffraction phenomena according to Fresnel

We can now turn to another facet in the study of light: the diffraction effects, the existence of which has already been mentioned. (See section 2 on the rectilinear propagation of light, and section 18 on the distribution of the light at the focal plane of a lens upon reduction of the size of the diaphragm). To explain such phenomena, the great physicist and optician, Augustin Fresnel (1788–1827) developed a theory of the propagation of light, with which we begin our discussion.

Until now we have used as a model for the propagation of light the principle of Huygens, which we define as follows. One can imagine a wave front to originate out of the previous one by supposing each point in the latter to be a secondary source of spherical waves. The envelope of these spherical waves forms the new wave front. Notice that here, in contrast to our previous formulation of Huygens' principle (see section 4) we are talking in the language of waves. But we have in the meantime discovered that waves show interference. Fresnel's addition to Huygens' principle consists, as we shall see in the following, in this, that he takes account of these interference phenomena. We should add a word about the range of validity of Fresnel's theory. The electromagnetic theory of light, which we shall describe later on, explains diffraction effects in an unforced manner and is, on deeper examination, also more precise. But Fresnel's theory of diffraction does, in most instances, give the correct explanation even of details, and for this reason it is considered by opticians to be a useful working tool.

Consider a wavefront V, originally emitted at the point O (figure 58). After a certain time the light will reach a point P further out. Fresnel supposed this to happen as follows: from

98

Figures 58, 59 and 60. *Top* Diffraction according to Fresnel.
Middle Fresnel's zones. *Bottom* One separated zone.

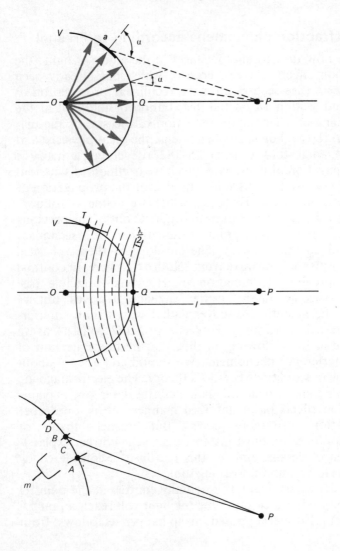

each piece *a* of the wave front light travels to *P*, and it must be remembered that the contribution from *b* arrives at *P* later than that from *a* if the distance from *b* to *P* is larger than the distance from *a* to *P*. Since both contributions derive from the same wave front *V* they must be considered as coherent. Fresnel further supposed that the contribution to the oscillation of the light at *P* is proportional to the surface of the piece that is contributing, such as each piece *a*, and inversely proportional to the distance from *a* to *P*. Finally, he supposed that the contribution is large if the angle *a* between the perpendicular at *a* and the line *aP* is small, and decreases as *a* increases.

It must be remembered that the energy of an oscillation is proportional to the square of the amplitude, the largest displacement. When, as above, we consider the contribution of each piece *a*, taking into account all the assumptions, and in particular taking into account the distance of each piece, such as *a* from *P*, we arrive at a remarkable result. This can be described as follows. It is unfortunately a somewhat long and complicated tale, but it cannot be shortened and is most easily understood with the aid of a recipe. Think of a sphere about *P* which just touches *V* at *Q* and call the distance *QP*, *l*. Imagine further other spheres with *P* as centre whose radii are respectively $\frac{1}{2}\lambda$, λ, $\frac{3}{2}\lambda$ ... $\frac{n\lambda}{2}$ larger than *l* (see figure 59).

These spheres cut *V* in circles. The annular surfaces between these circles we call *zones*. The area of such a zone is approximately equal to that of its neighbour and so all zones have approximately the same area as the inner one, which is the little cap around *Q*. If there are no obstructions or screens then all the zones in the wave front *V* contribute. The position of the last zone is determined by the tangent to *V*

Figures 61a and 61b. In (a) one sees
the diffraction pattern ad infinitum
produced by a number of small spheres,
whose shadows are seen in (b).

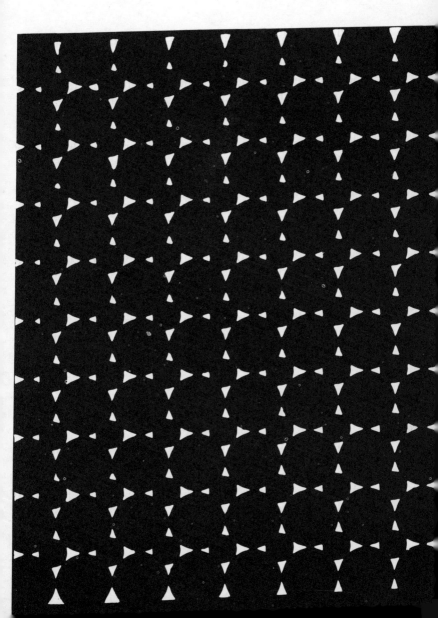

through P; T is a point thereof. The pieces around Q give the largest contribution while the zones close to T hardly contribute at all because for them the angle a is so large. If we look at one of the many zones, say the mth zone, then (see figure 60) we discover that because of the construction of the zones, BP is $\frac{1}{2}\lambda$ larger than AP and each sub-zone such as C has a corresponding sub-zone D such that DP is $\frac{1}{2}\lambda$ larger than CP. On the other hand something similar happens in the further half of the mth zone. Since to each sub-zone in the mth zone there is evidently another sub-zone which is just $\frac{1}{2}\lambda$ further or closer to P, the whole zone is destroyed through interference. Of the whole wave front only the inner half of the first zone remains, a circular region around Q in figure 59.

Considered in this way we see that there is associated with the propagation of light from V to P a *light ray* OQ with a certain width, which is determined by the size of the inner half of the first Fresnel zone. A numerical example: let OQ and QP both be one meter, and then the diameter of the inner half of the first zone is one millimetre.

If a part of V is screened off, one can calculate what the intensity at a point such as P will be by working out which part of the zones remain. The agreement with the observed diffraction figures, of which figure 61 gives an example, is always satisfactory. One cannot expect more from an approximate theory such as we have sketched here.

A singular case does deserve further mention. Suppose that P is such a distance from the round opening A in figure 62 that exactly two and a half zones are let through. Two zones knock each other out, leaving half a zone, exactly as much as if the wave front had not been obstructed at all. If precisely two (or three or any other whole number) zones are allowed through then there will be complete darkness at P.

Figures 62 and 63. *Top* Diffraction
by a circular opening.
Bottom. Diffraction by a disc.

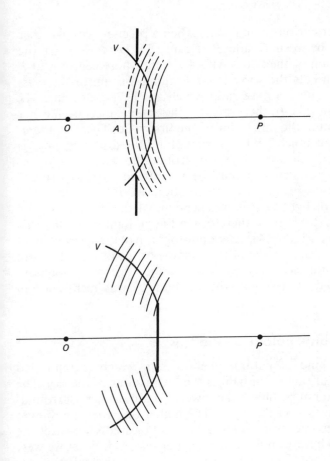

Another curious case occurs when a precisely circular disc is placed between O and P (figure 63). Here we start the construction of the zones with a sphere whose centre is at P and which cuts the wave front V along the rim of the disc. The other spheres have radii which are 1, 2, 3 etc. times $\frac{1}{2}\lambda$ larger than this. In this case also the zones cancel each other out excepting the inner half of the first zone. There is, therefore, just as much light at P as without the disc. If the eye is placed at P, one sees a light rim around the disc.

The experiment can only be performed with a perfectly round disc. From the construction, it follows that the presence of light at P is independent of the distance of the disc from P. There is, therefore, a line of light along the axis of the disc. Figure 64 shows a photograph of the speck of light precisely in the middle of the shadow of the disc. Just before sunrise on a clear day one can see the edge of a mountain surrounded by a similar rim of light, as was mentioned in section 2.

27 The blue colour of the sky

Another kind of natural phenomenon which is connected with the diffraction of light is the blue colour of the sky. The sky would not be blue if there were no atmosphere surrounding the surface of the earth. The higher one goes the thinner the air becomes until at a height of a hundred kilometres the density is but one millionth of that at sea level. What we were previously told as a fact which could not be proved, but only theorised about, namely that at such heights the sky is no longer blue nor even light, but dark, the astronauts have since been able to verify. One might suppose that the dust particles in the air when illuminated by the sunlight are

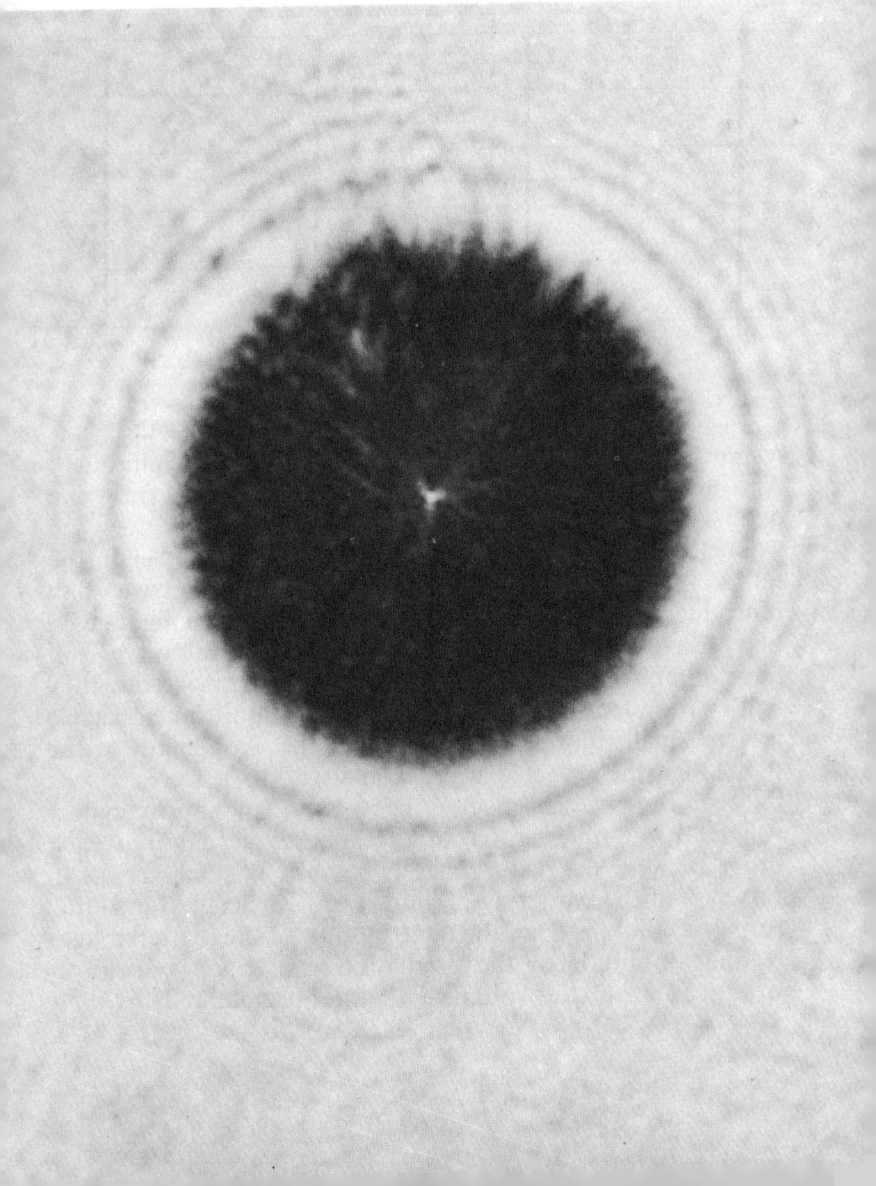

Figure 64. The light centre of a diffraction pattern from a distance.

Figure 65a. The scattering of light at an obstacle.

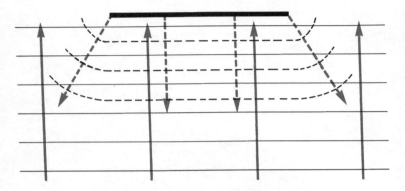

responsible for the light in the sky. But why is this light blue? And why does it become a deeper blue as we go from the depths to the higher mountain peaks?

One of the first to think about this was Lord Rayleigh (the father – the son also was a great physicist) and we shall reproduce the main points of his argument. If, as in figure 65a, plane wave fronts hit a flat obstacle, the reflected waves will have an approximately flat profile, although, it is true, they will be rounded-off at the edges by diffraction. If the obstacle is very small, however, smaller than the wavelength of the light, then the reflected wave fronts will, as it were, consist only of these 'edge effects'. They are then approximately spherical and the centres of the spheres lie close to each other because the disturbance is very small. One speaks in this case of the scattering of light. Lord Rayleigh argued that for very small particles the contribution of the scattered light to the amplitude of the oscillation at a point r away, is proportional to the volume v of the obstacle and inversely proportional to r. The contribution is also proportional to the amplitude of the light falling on the obstacle. The ratio of the two amplitudes of the incoming and the scattered light must be a dimensionless quantity. Since v/r is a volume (that is to say length to the third power) divided by a length, a factor must appear in the denominator with the dimensions of length squared; the only remaining length in the process of scattering which could conceivably play a role is the wavelength. The contribution to the amplitude is, therefore, inversely proportional to the square of the wavelength and the contribution to the intensity (which, of course, is proportional to the square of the amplitude) is proportional to $1/\lambda^4$. The intensity of the scattered light is, therefore, much larger for violet and blue light than it is for red or orange light, whose wavelengths are longer.

What are these obstructions, which are smaller than the wavelength of light? They are not dust particles; these would be too big. There remains one other possibility. A gas, and therefore also air, consists of molecules in large numbers. In one cubic centimetre of atmospheric air there are thirty trillion (3×10^{19}) molecules. In a small cube whose sides are one tenth of the wavelength of (violet) light (that is about four hundred nanometers) there are still two thousand molecules. These travel in random directions with great speed and, by collision with each other, they change their direction and speed constantly. Each molecule by itself is so small that it cannot affect the propagation of the light waves. In large numbers they are, however, able to slow down the light slightly. That is to say that the speed of light in air is somewhat less than it is in a vacuum: air has a refractive index n equal to the ratio of the speed of light in a vacuum to that in air. The refractive index of air (at a barometric pressure of

Figure 65b. The diffraction pattern from a zone plate. The coloured picture is the diffraction pattern obtained with an aperture made up of concentric rings – a so-called zone plate. Whenever a zone plate Z and a point light source L are set up as shown in the drawing, a pattern like the one shown in colour can be seen on the screen S. The sharp lines are due to a crossed wire reference mark on the same screen S. A displacement of Z causes a greater displacement of the centre M of the diffraction pattern such that the direction of the optical axis LM is changed. This apparatus can be used to place points accurately on a straight line, a process referred to as alignment. The straight line LM can be several tens of metres long. By using a laser as a light source, one can even observe displacements of a fraction of a millimetre over a distance of one kilometre.

760 mm of Mercury and at a temperature of 15°C) equals 1·00028 and it is also slightly dependent on the wavelength. As long as we have to deal with a very large number of molecules, such as for example the number in one cubic centimetre, we can be sure that their effect will be constant; the deviations from the mean of the number of molecules will always be unnoticeable. The story is quite different if we are dealing with a small volume such as we mentioned above. Deviations from the mean value of 2,000 are constantly occurring through the haphazard excess or deficiency of a dozen or several dozen molecules. With the help of the

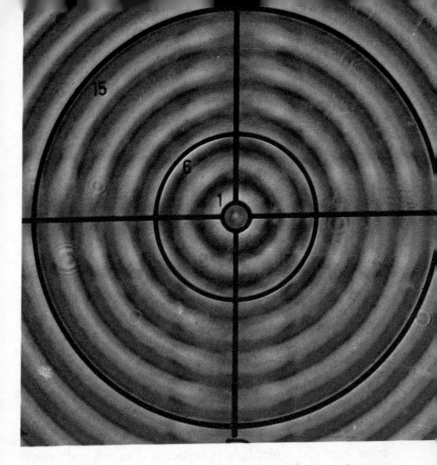

science of statistics one can work out how often how large a deviation from the mean will occur for a given very small volume. An excess above the mean simulates an extra obstacle for the light waves, while a deficiency is equivalent to a reduction of the obstacle. These small and rapidly changing regions will now scatter the light and, because they are small compared with the wavelength of the light, but yet not infinitesimally small, scattering will be proportional to $1/\lambda^4$. The blue and violet parts of the light give more scattered light than the red and orange parts. The air illuminated by the sun produces (scattered) light, which contains more blue: the

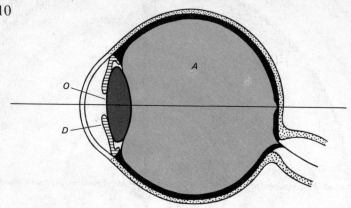

sky is blue. In the higher regions of the sky the number of molecules is smaller: the sky there is darker but a more beautiful and deeper blue. Dutchmen live at sea level in an atmosphere which, apart from the above-named density variations, also contains small dust particles and small water droplets. These are so large that the scattering, or more precisely the reflection of the light, is no longer much larger for smaller wavelengths. The light of the sky there is then much less coloured than it is for example in the higher mountain regions of Switzerland. When the sunlight travels through thick layers of air, such as at sunrise and sunset, more blue and violet light is scattered than red and yellow. When the sun is low down in the sky the sunlight is red.

In connection with this discussion about the light of the sky, we have one observation to make about the colour of the human eye. Without going into the peculiarities of the eye, we wish to mention only that the space A (figure 66), which is otherwise closed off from light, only receives light through the round opening O in a diaphragm D (the iris).

This opening, which we see as a small black speck in the middle of the eye, is called the pupil. The iris contains cells having light-absorbing material, the so-called pigment cells. No light goes through the iris (except in the case of albinos).

Figure 66. Diagram of an eye.   111

The front part of the iris contains a layer of cells which some-times have colouring matter in them. This causes the iris of of brunettes to be a dark brown. If the colouring matter is missing in the layer, then one might expect to see a black ring round the pupil. But the small sub-structures in the cell scatter the light and, because they are so small, the blue light is scattered more than the yellow or the red. Against the darker background of the black pigment cells the back of the iris, therefore, reflects in the main blue light – it is a blue eye.

28 Diffraction phenomena according to Fraunhofer

Another way of describing diffraction effects was developed by the German physicist Josef Fraunhofer (1787–1826). We consider first a long row of light sources oscillating equally together, such as in figure 68, and consider how the light emanating from these sources will interfere. In the figure we have shown by circles the crests of the waves emanating from the separate sources. What will the overall wavefront look like now? We remember that according to the discussion of section 5, a wavefront is a surface on which the oscillations have the same phase at each point. More briefly: wavefronts are surfaces of equal phase. In the cross-section given in the figure the wavefronts become lines which are tangential to the drawn circles. For at each point of contact the oscillation has, at that moment, reached its largest deviation; the points are, therefore, mutually in phase. We may, therefore, take a line such as V_0 in figure 68, parallel to the row of sources, as a wavefront; but there are also wavefronts which are not parallel to the row of sources, such as V_1, V_2, etc. From the row of sources there emerges one wavefront parallel to the row and two beams of wavefronts moving towards the sides.

Figure 67. Four orders of a spectrum.
For clarity, the separate orders are shown
under the spectrum.

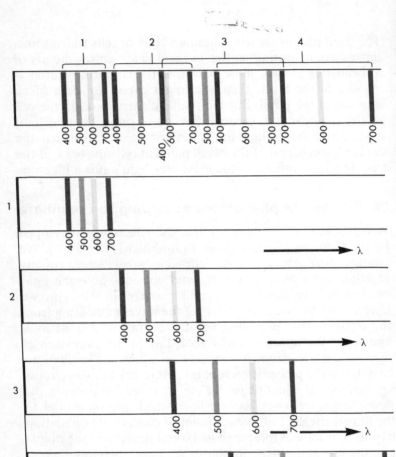

We can easily calculate at which angle these wavefronts emerge. The distance between a source Q (see figure 69) and the point P where the crest of a wave emitted by Q touches the front that goes through the source R, must be a whole number of wavelengths: all the sources are in phase, P must be in phase with the source R and, therefore, P must have the same phase as Q. Thus we can write down an expression for for the angle a_m which a wavefront 'of the m-th order' makes with the row of sources.

$$\sin a_m = \frac{m\lambda}{p}$$

in which p is the distance between two sources. Some readers may now protest: alright, there is always a crest at the points of contact of the spherical waves emitted by different sources (points such as P or S in figure 69) with the constructed wavefronts; but what happens between these points of contact? Our protesting readers are quite right: the construction we have sketched is only an approximation. Suppose we consider the situation from a long way off: then the spaces between two points of contact, such as P and S, become smaller and smaller; the further away we position ourselves the better it becomes: the approximation is valid 'in the limit of an infinite distance' as a mathematician would put it.

With the help of this construction originally derived by Fraunhofer, we shall now look at the diffraction from a narrow opening. We look, therefore, at figure 70. A plane wavefront V falls on a screen S in which there is a slit with its length perpendicular to the surface of the drawing. The separate points along the slit AB are to be considered as a row of very closely spaced light sources with equal phase. If we now draw an arbitrary line AC at an angle to AB then this

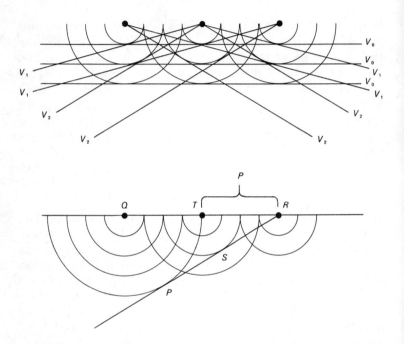

Figures 68 and 69. *Top* Wavefronts produced by a row of light sources. *Bottom* One of the wavefronts.

cannot be a wavefront, according to our previous construction. For all the sources in the slit are a different distance away from this line, so that AC does not have the same phase all along it. We must, however, remember that Fraunhofer's theory is only valid in the limit of infinitely large distance to the slit. We therefore go and stand at infinity, or equivalently, we bring together at the focal plane T of the lens L all the light rays emanating from the slit in a direction perpendicular to AC. All these rays interfere at the surface T; if AC were a wavefront, all the amplitudes coming from AC would build up at P, and an image would be formed there. This is the case in figure 70 when AC lies along AB; the light then arrives at P_0 together. We now investigate the intensity at the focal plane due to the light rays which travel perpendicularly to the line AC and are brought together at the point P of the focal plane of the lens L when AC makes an angle with the surface of the slit AB. Suppose that this angle a is such that the distance BC is equal to λ. At the points between C and A the distance through which a light ray perpendicular to AC travels from the slit becomes continually smaller, the closer one comes to A. That is to say that when the same phase is present all along AB, the phase along AC changes evenly until at C the oscillation is again in phase with A. If we now take an instantaneous picture of the amplitude of the light oscillations along AC, at a time when those at A and C are precisely at the equilibrium distance with zero amplitude, then we will see the picture shown in figure 71a. At the point P of the focal plane of the lens L (figure 70) all these amplitudes interfere. We see that there are as many negative as positive amplitudes along AC; these added up at P give precisely zero which means that there is a dark spot of our diffraction image at P. We can use the same argument whenever the distance BC is a whole number times the wavelength λ. For the case when BC equals 4λ, the amplitude distribution along AC (at the moment that the amplitude at A and C is zero) is as shown in figure 71b. One can see from this that, in this case also positive and negative amplitudes cancel each other out. Thus, in general:

whenever $\sin a = \dfrac{n\lambda}{P}$, where P is the width of the slit, there is

darkness in the corresponding place of the focal plane. Simple optical theory of image formation shows us that the distance x from P to the middle of the diffraction pattern equals af, (for small values of a), where f is the focal length of the lens

Figures 70 and 71. *Top* Diffraction
at a slit according to Fraunhofer. The lens *L*
focusses the parallel rays of light on to
the focal plane *T*. *Bottom* Variation of
the amplitude along the line *AC*.

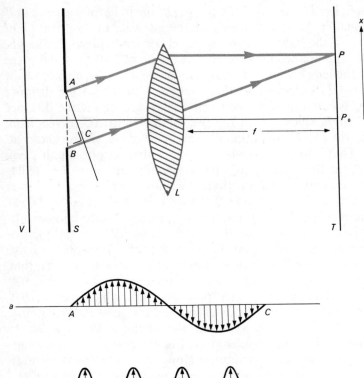

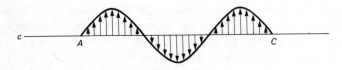

Figure 72. The intensity distribution
at the focal plane.

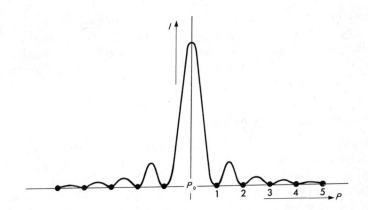

L. A different situation obtains when the distance BC in
figure 70 equals an odd number of half wavelengths: $\frac{1}{2}\lambda$,
$\frac{3}{2}\lambda$, $\frac{5}{2}\lambda$, etc. In figure 71c we have drawn the amplitude
distribution along AC for BC equal to $\frac{3}{2}\lambda$, again when the
amplitude at A is zero; we see that upon addition of all the
amplitudes along AC a surplus remains: two half periods of
the amplitude distribution cancel each other out, leaving the
third. In the focal plane of L there is, therefore, a light spot.
The intensity is not, however, as large as at the point P_0,
where all the amplitudes of AB added up together. If we
analyse the situation for each value of the distance BC we
find an intensity distribution in the focal plane of L such as is
shown in figure 72. We have taken the unit of length there as
$\frac{\lambda f}{P}$. The digit 2 in this figure corresponds, therefore, to the
value of 2λ for BC in figure 70. One can compare the intensity

distribution in figure 72 with the diffraction pattern of Airy, which we found experimentally in section 18. We see that the diameter of the figure is inversely proportional to the width P of the opening AB in the screen S (figure 70) and directly proportional to the wavelength λ.

29 Diffraction gratings

A closely allied subject is that of diffraction gratings. These instruments are not only of theoretical interest but also of great practical importance, as will become clear from the following. We begin by considering a grating which consists of evenly spaced strips, which alternately let the light through and stop it. Those that transmit the light once again form a row of sources such as we have been discussing in the previous pages in connection with Fraunhofer's theory of diffraction. We allow a plane wavefront V to fall upon the row. Here again there is not only a wavefront moving in the direction of the incoming light but also in those directions for which the path difference from the different sources is precisely a whole number of wavelengths. These plane wavefronts can be refocussed in the focal plane of the lens L (figure 73), at the points P and Q. In that focal plane there will, therefore, be a number of maxima which all derive from V and belong to the given wavelength.

If the wavelength is changed, the directions of the maxima are also changed. The mth maximum is found where the path difference from two neighbouring slits is a whole number m times the wavelength. One refers to it as the diffraction image of the mth order. Since the maxima for different wavelengths come next to each other, we obtain a spectrum, indeed several spectra, of the first order, the second order, and so on.

Figure 73. How a grating works.

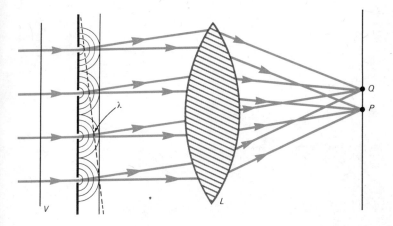

It is rather a nuisance that these orders overlap. For where the wavelength 380 nm has its second order maximum, that of 760 nm has its first order maximum. Where 400 nm has its fifth order maximum 500 nm reaches its fourth order maximum, and so on. In figure 67 we have drawn the relative positions of the first, second and third order maxima for four wavelengths out of the visible spectrum. This phenomenon coincides, incidentally, with the overlapping of the colours in Newton's rings made with white light. There is so far no particular reason for rejoicing. The light is spread out in several spectra, but how finely, how sharply are the spectral lines depicted? *That* is an important property of a spectroscope, for it determines how close the wavelengths of two lines may be, while still being distinguishable.

A remarkable fact now emerges. It is nowadays possible to make gratings with a regularity and a fineness which is difficult to describe in a few words. These gratings do not transmit the light, but reflect it (figure 74; in this figure are

120

Figure 74. A reflection grating.

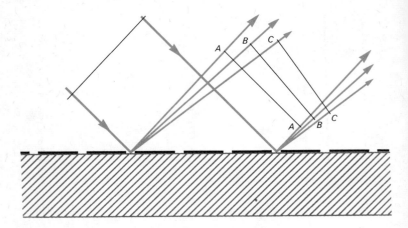

drawn the reflected wavefront *AA* and the first and second order fronts *BB* and *CC*). By making scratches on a reflecting surface one obtains alternately reflecting and non-reflecting strips and a reasoning analogous to that employed above for the transmitting grating shows that here also diffraction maxima and spectra are formed.

The scratches are made with a specially shaped diamond. After each scratch the mirror surface that is to be scratched is moved at right angles to the scratch and it is possible to make as many as a hundred thousand straight scratches on a mirror with a regularity much better than one ten thousandth of a millimetre. There are on such a reflection grating 600, 800 or even 1200 scratches per millimetre, each five or more centimetres long and each scratch having a good profile. It goes without saying that very special measuring apparatus must be used to obtain such accuracies. The slide upon which the mirror lies, and which must be constantly moved up to be able to make the next scratch, is moved by a screw. The making of this screw is in itself the work of many months, because it has to be so regular. The steps themselves are controlled with an interferometer coupled to the slide. The whole work takes place in a room which is kept at a precisely controlled temperature. The pressure with which the diamond cuts must also be kept constant. The material of the mirror – optical glass which is afterwards covered with a mirroring aluminium surface and coating – and also all the material of which the various parts of the machine are made must all be of the best quality. The whole operation is performed completely automatically; no human body, which can give warmth out to the surrounding air, must be close-by. Those are some of the conditions needed to make a good grating. That the price is not impossibly high is due to the relatively large production of this remarkable optical part.

There are then, to take up the thread of our story, a large number of 'reflecting slits'. We recall that in one direction for which the path difference between two adjacent slits is $m\lambda$ (m is a whole number), there is a maximum. In a direction, however, which is only slightly different from this, namely such that the path difference is $m\lambda$ plus $0 \cdot 00001\lambda$ there will already be darkness. The light coming from the slit number 50001 has a path difference relative to the first slit of $m\lambda$ plus $0 \cdot 50000\lambda$. The waves coming from these two slits cancel each other out: the crests of the light of the first slit coincide with the troughs of that coming from the 50001th. The same is the case for the second and the slit number 50002. On the other side of the maximum also it will rapidly get dark, namely where the path difference for the light from two adjacent slits is $m\lambda$ minus $0 \cdot 00001\lambda$.

We cannot here go into the explanation of why there are

Figure 75. Photographs of spectra for helium (He), iron (Fe) and mercury (Hg). The wavelengths of a few of the mercury lines are indicated.

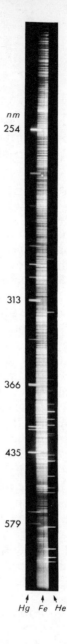

nm

254

313

366

435

579

Hg Fe He

Figure 76. Separation of two spectral
lines of wavelengths λ_1 and λ_2.

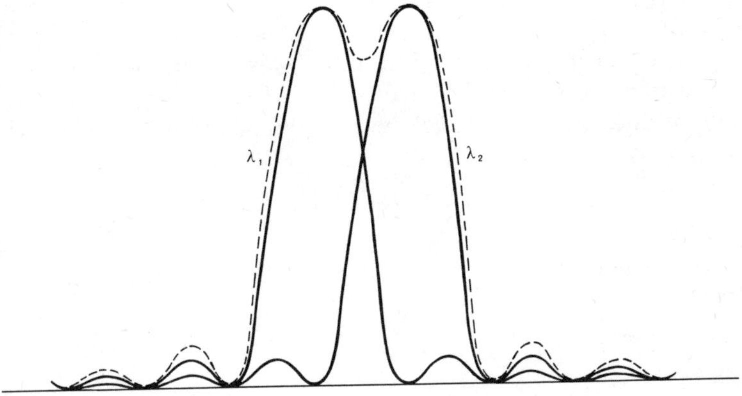

weak secondary maxima past the dark edges of the main
maxima, discussed above, but turn to figure 75 for a photograph of a few spectra, taken with a grating. The wavelengths (in nm) of some of the lines are marked on the figure.

There is one concept which we must make clear, which
plays a great role in the science of spectroscopy: the *resolving
power*. Suppose that we have to deal with two spectral lines,
whose wavelengths λ_1 and λ_2 differ slightly. In the spectrum,
formed with a grating, the intensity distribution of each is as
given in figure 76. These, approximately equally bright, lines
are depicted so close to each other that the maximum of λ_2
is just in the same direction as the neighbouring minimum of
λ_1. The intensity of both lines together is indicated by the
dotted line. Between the two maxima in this overall intensity
distribution there is a depression. In practice it appears that
in such a case the lines can still be seen as a doublet; one can
still just distinguish them. In our example of the mth maximum, formed by a grating with one hundred thousand lines,
one gets on the one hand a minimum for λ_1 in the direction
which is equivalent to a path difference of $m\lambda_1$ plus $0 \cdot 00001\lambda_1$,

on the other hand the maximum for λ_2 is just in the direction for which the path difference is $m\lambda_2$. If we equate these two magnitudes then the wavelength difference that one can just resolve is seen to be

$$\lambda_1 - \lambda_2 = \frac{0\cdot00001\lambda_1}{m}.$$

More generally we can say: if the grating has N scratches then

$$\lambda_1 - \lambda_2 = \frac{\lambda_1}{mN}.$$

The fraction $\frac{\lambda_1}{\lambda_2 - \lambda_1}$ one calls the resolving power R and we see that R equals mN. The larger R is, the smaller is the wavelength difference that can just be distinguished. This is a remarkably simple outcome. R is the product of the order m of the spectrum and the number N of the scratches and depends on no other factor, not even on the fineness of the scratches.

One might for an instant think that one could then obtain the same resolving power with a hundred thousand concrete posts. And this would indeed be the case, if the distances between the posts could be made precisely the same to within one ten thousandth of a millimetre or better. There is yet another disadvantage of a gross grating: the spread of the spectrum becomes larger the smaller the distance between the scratches, as is clear from figure 73. When the ratio of the distance between the sources and the wavelength is reduced, the wavefront shown by the dotted line will come off at a larger angle.

For gratings such as we have been talking about so far, one needs a preliminary optical component to make the light

Figures 77a and 77b. *Top* A concave grating according to Rowland. *Bottom* A different arrangement for a concave grating.

125

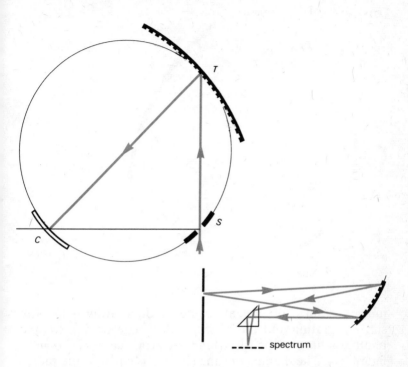

spectrum

falling on the grating into a parallel beam. This part of the apparatus is called a collimator. The diffracted light that is transmitted or reflected, as the case may be, must pass through a second optical component in order that each spectral line shall be properly depicted in the focal plane. The gratings were flat ones. Rowland, who has played an important role in the development of the making of gratings, had the idea of making gratings in mirror surfaces which were not flat. He took a perfectly spherical hollow mirror and cut a grating on it. With this one modification the collimator and

126

Figure 78. A spectrophotometer.

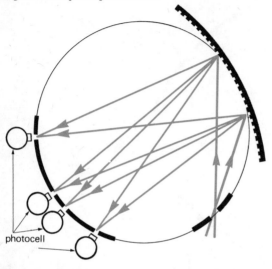

photocell

image-forming components could be done away with. The slit, the grating and the photographic plate or film for the photographing of the spectrum were arranged as is shown in figure 77a. The diameter of the circle C is equal to the radius of curvature of the mirror grating T, the slit S is placed on this circle and the spectrum is also formed on it. A great practical advantage is obtained with this arrangement: now that the lenses are superfluous, one no longer has to be afraid of making his researches in the far ultra-violet or the far infra-red regions of radiation which are not transmitted by glass. Many characteristic spectral lines are found just out-side the visible part of the spectrum and the whole region of the spectrum now becomes available for study.

Many other arrangements are also possible for forming spectra with a hollow grating. A particularly beautiful set-up is shown in figure 77b. In the above mentioned cases the spectrum was photographed. The instruments were spectrographs. Figure 78 shows a 'spectrophotometer'. At the place where the spectrum is formed there is a screen with slit-like openings at the places where the images of the spectral lines are formed, characteristic of particular atoms. If one evaporates an element in an electrical discharge the atoms thereof emit light with completely specified wavelength. The intensity of the lines is furthermore a measure of the concentration of the element. So one can determine the presence and the relative concentration of an element, if one sets up photocells behind the slits. These give an electric current proportional to the light falling upon them.

5 Polarisation

30 Polarisation

As if these properties of light, which we have so far briefly mentioned, were not enough, light has a whole series of other remarkable properties which are admittedly rather more complex, but which we nevertheless must mention. Both their physical background and their practical uses are of sufficient importance. We refer here to the polarisation of light and to the phenomenon of double refraction in crystals.

To start with, an experiment. Let a beam of light fall on a reflecting surface under a large angle of incidence; we shall return to a discussion of the size of this angle (figure 79). The mirror must be made not of metal but of glass. To avoid difficulties concerned with the reflection from the front and back sides of the glass, we take black glass. The reflecting surface is flat and well polished and has no coating or any other layers on it. It is also very clean.

The perpendicular N at the point of incidence on the reflecting surface and the direction p of the incoming beam together determine the surface of incidence V. The direction q of the reflected beam also lies in this surface. In figure 80a we have drawn a second mirror of the same kind for which the incoming beam is q. The normal M at the point of incidence with the second mirror lies in the same plane V, and the angle of incidence is the same as for the first mirror. V is therefore also the plane of incidence for the reflection at the second mirror, so that the ray s reflected by this mirror also lies in V. It is found that s has a certain intensity, which is small, but by no means zero. We now start turning the second mirror about q. The beam s reflected by the second mirror, then describes a cone with q as axis. As we turn the mirror the intensity of s becomes smaller, and this beam even

Figures 79 and 80. *Top* A mirror made of
black glass. *Bottom* Three positions of two mirrors
relative to one another. In (a) the
surfaces of incidence coincide, in (b) they are
perpendicular, and in (c) they coincide again.

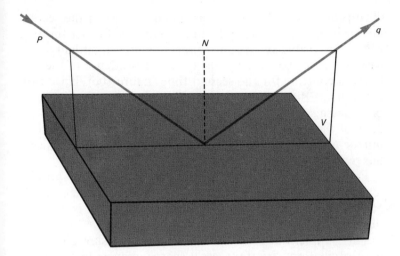

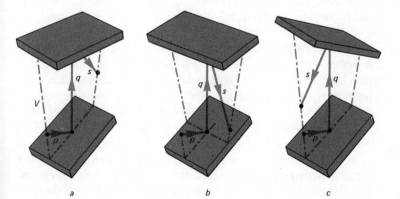

disappears completely (has zero intensity), when the second mirror is turned through 90° (figure 80b). On further turning, *s* becomes visible again and regains the intensity it had in the case of figure 80a, when the surfaces of incidence of the two mirrors coincide for the second time (figure 80c). If we turn the mirror further through 270°, then the intensity of *s* becomes again zero. By turning right through 360° we are back at the initial position. Since we have turned the second mirror about *q*, the angle of incidence at the second mirror has remained the same throughout.

For ordinary (black) glass the refractive index is approximately 1·52. The angle of incidence must be made equal to 56°40′ in order to succeed in the experiment, that is to say in order to see *s* disappear in the positions *b* and *d*.

This simple, but fundamental, experiment shows that the light oscillations are transversal (perpendicular to the direction of movement). If there were any oscillation in the direction of motion then on turning about *q* there would always remain a small intensity even in the positions *b* and *d*. Light oscillations have no component in the direction of motion; they have no longitudinal component. This is in contrast to sound waves in gases which are purely longitudinal.

A closer examination shows that for the given angle of incidence only those oscillations are reflected which, apart from being transversal to the direction of motion, are also transversal to the plane of incidence. Accepting this we can understand that in the case shown in figure 80b *s* must disappear, since the oscillations in the beam reflected by the first mirror are perpendicular to the plane *V* so that upon arrival at the second mirror they lie in the plane of incidence for the second mirror and cannot be reflected by it. In the cases *a* and *c* the planes of incidence of both mirrors coincide and there is, therefore, no difficulty for reflection by the second mirror. For any non-metallic material one can find an angle at which this phenomenon occurs, the so-called Brewster angle i_B. We can write the simple trigonometric formula

$$\tan i_B = n$$

where n is the refractive index of the mirror.

Beams of light in which oscillations occur only in one direction are described as *linearly polarised* and the plane through the beam axis perpendicular to the direction of oscillation is called the *plane of polarisation*. In figure 81 q is linearly polarised and V is the plane of polarisation. The first black mirror in figure 80 is called a polariser. Of the light falling upon it with transverse oscillations in all directions, it selects linearly polarised light. There are also other kinds of polarised light. We will not tire the reader with a detailed description of these, nor of how they can be obtained or detected as such. In all kinds of polarised light the oscillations are perpendicular to the direction of motion. If one considers the oscillations as the motion of small fictitious particles (in a manner analogous to the motion of the cork on the surface of the water discussed in section 5), then instead of just motion up and down, such as would correspond to linearly polarised light, one can also think of oscillations which are circular, or elliptical. In figure 82 a 'snapshot' is shown of a beam of circularly polarised light. The small 'particle' A moves in a circle about its equilibrium position A_0; the surface of the circle is perpendicular to the direction of motion a. The position at one instant in time is given in the figure for a number of oscillating 'particles' B, C, etc. The rotation of each 'particle' can have two directions. If one looks into the beam (in the figure, this would be from the right) and the 'particles' are moving clockwise, then the beam is called *right-circularly polarised*. If the 'particles' are moving anti-clockwise, then one speaks of *left-circularly polarised* light (see figure 83).

31 Double refraction

Going over now to a description of double refraction, we begin once again with a simple experiment. We need a piece of calcite, which is a crystal of calcium carbonate, found here and there in reasonably large and clear pieces, although it must immediately be added that the world's supply of beautiful pieces is, unfortunately, fast dwindling. The pieces of calcite are easily split in certain directions determined by the internal structure of the crystal. If necessary the split pieces can also be ground and polished. If we put such a crystal on a piece of paper with a black dot on it, then when looking through the crystal we see two dots. If we turn the crystal about an axis perpendicular to the paper, one of the dots remains in the same position while the other describes a circle about it (figure 84). If we look in a direction perpendicular to the sheet of paper then the 'stationary' image is in the position it would have been in without the crystal, whereas the other is displaced to one side. The experiment becomes even clearer if the crystal is placed on a black piece of paper which has a small hole in it and which is illuminated from below (figure 85), when two light dots are seen. It is as if the light from the hole can go in two directions: straight upwards and obliquely through the crystal. The paths of the light beams are shown in the figure. Even if we look obliquely at the crystal, we see two images. There is double refraction. The

Figures 81, 82 and 83. *Top* Plane polarised light. 133
Middle Circularly polarised light.
Bottom Left and right circularly polarised light.

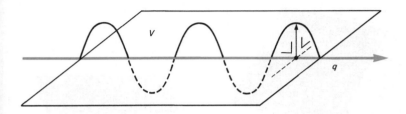

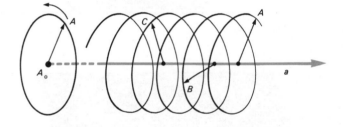

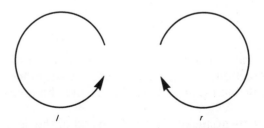

Figures 84, 85 and 86. *Top* When the crystal is turned, one of the images rotates about the other.
Middle Side view of the crystal. The beam *o* oscillates in the plane of the paper, and *e* perpendicularly to it.
Bottom Nicol's polarising prism. The ordinary ray is totally reflected on to the side surface.

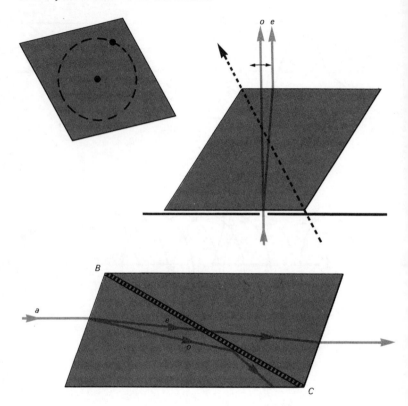

stationary ray is shown, upon investigation, to obey Snell's law of refraction, whereas the other behaves differently. The first we call the *ordinary ray*, the second the *extra-ordinary* ray.

We have by no means reached the end of the description of

the curious phenomena which occur in calcite crystals. If we take two such crystals, one on top of the other, we see one, two or four images, depending on the orientation of the upper crystal with respect to the lower one. Whenever the opportunity arises to perform this experiment one is always fascinated by the surprising beauty of the result. It is as if nature has challenged us to discover an explanation for it. It is a fact that there is something else associated with double refraction: the two rays are polarised in mutually perpendicular directions. There is in the crystal a symmetry axis, of which the direction is shown in figure 85. In the direction of this axis the two images lie on top of each other. By allowing the beams belonging to each of these images to fall separately on the polarising mirror of figure 80a, one finds out that the plane in which the two beams lie, and which is parallel to the above-mentioned symmetry axis, plays an important role. The ordinary ray oscillates perpendicularly to this plane, the extraordinary ray oscillates in the plane. This plane is called the *principal plane*. It is as if a ray wishing to enter the crystal should meet a customs official who lays down the following rule:

You may come in, and you may either obey Snell's law, or follow another specified route. In the case that you do not oscillate in either of the required directions, we will have to decompose you into these two directions of oscillation and we will send the components according to the above-mentioned regulations.

Returning to figure 85, it is easy to see that out of 'natural' light (light that oscillates in all directions transverse to the direction of motion) a pair of linearly polarised beams can be obtained. If one screens off one of these beams, one has one linearly polarised beam left over. The screen and the crystal together form a polariser. Although calcite has a particularly large double refraction (there are not many materials which separate the two rays by such a large amount), it is very difficult to produce a wide beam of linearly polarised light in this way. A much more effective method is the following: a calcite crystal having an elongated shape (see figure 86) is sawn in the direction *BC*. The sawn surfaces are polished and after that the two pieces are stuck together with a transparent optical cement called Canada balsam. For the ordinary ray *o* the refractive index is 1·65 and the direction of the saw cut is chosen in such a manner that the ordinary ray, belonging to the incoming ray *a*, falls at such a large angle upon the cement surface that it is totally reflected. The totally reflected ray falls upon the blackened side and is absorbed. The extraordinary ray *e* has, however, a speed of propagation corresponding to a lower refractive index. It easily passes through the layer of cement and comes out of the far side oscillating in the principal plane, that is, the plane of the drawing. We have now obtained a single beam of linearly polarised light which is as wide as the crystal allows. Such a polarising prism is called a *Nicol prism*, after its discoverer.

With it we have an outstandingly good way of reducing the brightness of the beam by a measurable amount. For, if we place two Nicols one after the other, and if the directions of oscillation which they transmit make an angle *a* with each other, then the oscillation emerging from the first Nicol must be projected upon the direction of oscillation which is transmitted by the second one (figure 87). The ratio of the lines *q* and *p* is called cos *a* and can be found from tables. Since the intensity of light oscillation equals the square of the amplitude, the intensity of the beam emerging through the second Nicol bears a ratio to the intensity of the beam emerging from

Figures 87, 88 and 89. *Top* The first Nicol transmits
the oscillation *p*, the second Nicol transmits *q*.
Middle The wavefront in a crystal of calcite.
Bottom The wavefront in a crystal of quartz. The difference
between ellipse and circle has been much exaggerated
in this and in the preceding figure.

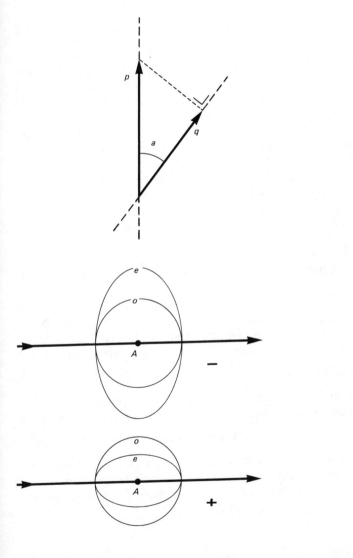

the first one of $\frac{q^2}{p^2}$ or $\cos^2 a$. Without going into any more details we simply state that, in a crystal such as calcite, light emanating from a point (figure 88) in a particular direction does so as follows. In each direction it has two directions of oscillation, to each of which corresponds a particular speed of propagation. After the passage of time the light emanating from A has arrived at the surface of a sphere *and* at that of an ellipsoid. The sphere corresponds to the ordinary ray, the ellipsoid to the extraordinary one. It is not possible to describe the refraction of the extraordinary ray without mathematical formulae. We must avoid these here but do wish to mention that the direction of the principal symmetry axis of the crystal is a peculiar one: in this direction there is only one speed of propagation. Rays travelling along it show no double refraction. There is no splitting into ordinary and extraordinary rays; and there is, therefore, no polarisation. Along it there is no customs barrier.

The difference in the speeds of propagation is largest in a direction perpendicular to the principal symmetry axis of the crystal. One ascribes two principal refractive indices to the crystal, n_o for the ordinary ray, n_e for the extraordinary one. For calcite n_o equals 1·66 and n_e equals 1·49. Another doubly refracting crystal, which is often used in optical experiments, is quartz (crystalised silicon dioxide). For this crystal n_o 1·544 and n_e is 1·553.* When n_e is larger than n_o the speed of propagation of the extraordinary ray is smaller than that of the ordinary ray. Crystals of the calcite type are called negative, and those of the quartz type positive. Figure 89 shows one of the latter kind.

32 Anisotropic media between polarisers

Materials in which light behaves in such a complicated fashion, are called *anisotropic* as opposed to the materials in which the speed of propagation is the same in all directions and in which there is, therefore, no double refraction. The latter we call *isotropic* (from the Greek: *isos* meaning 'equal', tropic from *trepein*, meaning 'turning'; behaving the same in all directions). The vacuum, gases, liquids, glass, diamond, kitchen salt crystals are all isotropic. Ruby, saphire and ice are anisotropic.

We have not exhausted the list of anisotropic crystals. There are many, much more complicated, kinds of optical anisotropy compared to which the effects in calcite and quartz are mere child's play. The vast majority of crystals possess the so-called bi-axial anistropy, about which we must, however, remain silent.

The optical properties are so characteristic that the determination and identification of minerals proceeds along optical lines. We can say a few more words about this. The crystals are, for this purpose, placed between two polarisers and, if they are small, also in a polarising microscope, which has a polariser between the microscope mirror and the object and a second polariser above the eyepiece.

First, another word about the polariser. Now that calcite is becoming rare and therefore expensive, people have looked for other ways of obtaining linearly polarised light from natural light. The mineral tourmaline provided the first clue of the means whereby this could be achieved. This anisotropic crystal not only exhibits double refraction but also has the property that one of the two rays (the extraordinary) passes through practically unhindered, while the other (the

140

Figures 90a and 90b. Removal of reflections by polaroid.

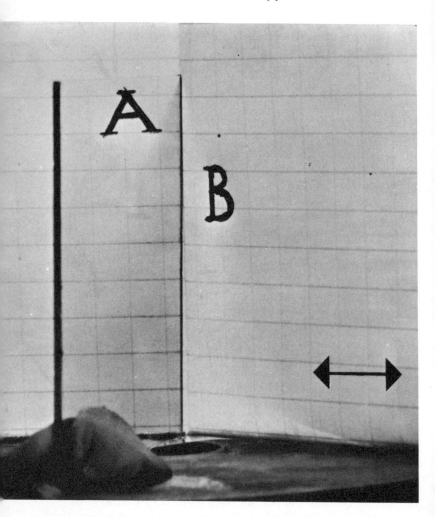

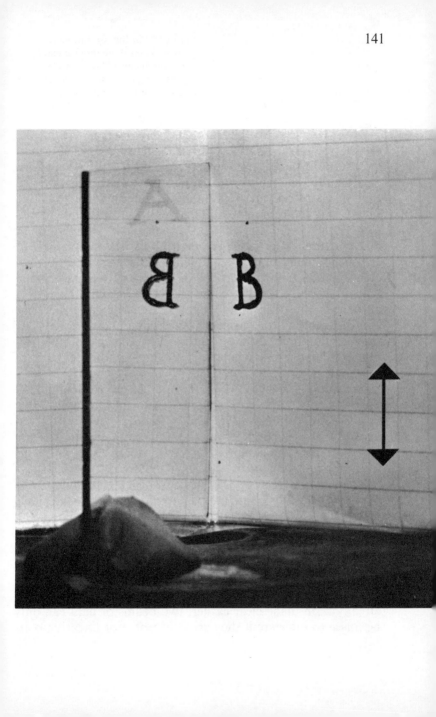

ordinary) is absorbed. Only one ray emerges from the crystal and this is linearly polarised. The crystals of tourmaline found in nature are, however, rather small. A new idea emerged. In the manufacture of plastics it was already known that sheets of polymerised material, materials that thus had rather long molecules, could be made to show double refraction if they were stretched at a particular phase of their manufacture. After much research it has become possible to attach iodine atoms to the long molecules of polyvinyl alcohol in such a way that one of the two rays is transmitted with practically no loss while the other is quite effectively absorbed. The transmitted light is linearly polarised. The sheets exhibiting this property were called polaroid sheets by the manufacturers. Many experiments in the field of polarisation of light are nowadays performed with the help of polaroid, or sheet polarisers.

For that matter they also come into use quite often in daily life. Not only do polaroid spectacles transmit light with only one direction of oscillation, and of that only two thirds, but all sorts of reflections from water and glass windows are visibly reduced in intensity, as is shown in figure 90. This follows from the fact that the light reflected from such surfaces is more or less polarised: oscillations perpendicular to the plane of incidence are more intense than those in the plane. For water surfaces the plane of incidence for sunlight is vertical. If the sheets of the polaroid spectacle are oriented such that only vertical oscillations are transmitted, the reflection of the sun in the water is much reduced.

After this diversion we leave the sheet polarisers and turn our thoughts to the interference of polarised light. As has already been made clear earlier, two beams of light can only be made to interfere if they are coherent. For linearly polar-

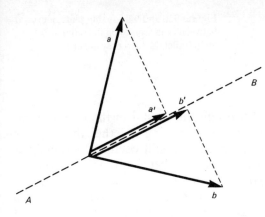

ised light another condition must also be fulfilled. If the directions of oscillation of the two beams are the same, one obtains precisely the same interference phenomena as with natural light, but if the oscillations are perpendicular to each other, the two beams do not interfere (not even if they are coherent). By using a trick, however, it is possible in the latter case to obtain interference. Suppose two coherent beams come towards us from out of the surface of the drawing (figure 91), with directions of oscillation which are mutually perpendicular. Before the beams reach our eyes, we let them go through a polariser which only transmits oscillations in the direction AB. Of the oscillations a and b falling upon it, only the projections on to AB are transmitted, respectively a' and b'. These two components oscillate in the same direction and *now* it is possible to observe interference between the two beams.

Because the polariser makes possible the observation of interference phenomena, and thereby gives us the possibility of measuring the path difference between the two original beams, it is called an *analyser* (it gives us the possibility of analysing phenomena associated with the light). Which then are the interference phenomena one can see?

Allow linearly polarised white light from a polariser P to fall on anisotropic crystal plate. The projections of the oscilla-

Figures 92a and 92b. A thin plate of crystal
between polarisers. *Top* the polarisers
are parallel. *Bottom* they are crossed.

tions are transmitted through the crystal in the two allowed directions. These two beams travelling together through the crystal emerge from the plate and still oscillate perpendicularly to each other. We must remember that the two directions of oscillation correspond to different speeds of propagation through the crystal. One beam, therefore, falls a little behind the other. We now pass them both through the analyser A and here the projection of each of the two oscillations on to the allowed direction is transmitted. The beams can now interfere since we have succeeded in making them oscillate in the same direction and since the two beams have a common origin and are, therefore, coherent. Because there is a path difference between them, darkness can occur. For the wavelength λ for which the path difference is exactly $\frac{1}{2}\lambda$, or $\frac{1}{2}\lambda$ plus a whole number times λ there will be darkness; these colours are 'extinguished'. For colours for which the path difference is equal to a whole number times the wavelength there will be light. Because some of the colours are missing the light beam coming out of the analyser will not be white but coloured. The phenomenon is, therefore, called chromatic polarisation (from the Greek *chroma* meaning 'colour'). One usually orientates P and A such that the directions of oscillation which they transmit are either mutually perpendicular or parallel to each other. One speaks then of crossed and parallel Nicols respectively. Let us take the first case. The plate of crystal between the two polarisers is turned about the direction of observation. If the direction of oscillation of the light emanating from the polariser coincides with one of the two allowed directions for the crystal then the oscillations are not decomposed into two components. There is then no interference. The crossed polarisers on their own gave darkness; now with the plate between them in this

orientation it remains dark. There will be four such orientations of the plate which give darkness. Between these are the
positions when (coloured) light is visible. If the plate of
crystal is isotropic, there will never be any decomposition into
components. There is darkness in all orientations. This is the
best method for finding out whether a crystal is anisotropic.
One would never, in practice, succeed in doing so by trying
to see whether double refraction took place. The double
refraction is too small for this. The experiment described
above is, however, easy to do and completely satisfactory.
Furthermore the allowed directions of oscillation are also

Figures 93 and 94. *Left* Interference lines from a uni-axial crystal between crossed polarisers. *Below* The same for a bi-axial crystal.

easy to find. An example is shown in figure 92. Between two parallel (a) or crossed (b) polarisers there is placed a thin plate made by grinding and polishing a stone. The remarkably beautiful phenomena associated with chromatic polarisation are always fascinating. The possibilities of application are enormous. They are not, however, a simple matter to explain. Things become even more complicated if we shine a beam of light on to the crystal, not just from one direction but from many at the same time, in a so-called converging beam. To give an impression of what then occurs, we show in figures 93 and 94 respectively the result of placing a uni-axial or bi-axial crystal in convergent light between crossed polarisers. The mineralogist revels in the large amount of, to him, useful information which can be obtained in this way. He has the privilege and pleasure of daily working with such, often very beautifully coloured, pictures.

33 Induced anisotropy

Compared with what we have just described, what happens on reflection of polarised light at a metallic surface is really complicated. It is no coincidence that just those metals which are good electrical conductors behave differently optically from the non-conductors, such as glass and the crystals we have discussed so far. The atoms, molecules and ions which are the building blocks out of which all materials are made, contain electrically negatively charged electrons. In the light beams move fast oscillating electric and magnetic fields. It is, therefore, not surprising that the interaction between light and the electric charges in the materials is different in non-conductors, in which the electrons are more or less strongly bound at equilibrium positions, than in conductors, where at least some of the electrons have a large freedom of movement. We shall come back later to the theory of the interaction of light and matter.

The fact we noted previously that, by stretching, a plastic sheet could be made anisotropic is related to a phenomenon which is not uncommon. All isotropic materials which are stretched or compressed become anisotropic and the size of the double refraction is proportional to the stretching or pressing force. If the force is removed, the anisotropy disappears. Just as double refraction can be caused by outside forces acting on an isotropic material (mechanical pressure or stretching), so it is possible to cause the plane of polarisation to rotate artificially. This can be done by allowing a magnetic field to work on the material in such a way that the magnetic lines of force lie either in the direction of the light beams or in exactly the opposite direction. Carbon disulphide is a material for which this phenomenon can be observed. The phenomenon is called the *Faraday effect*, after its discoverer, who was always interested in investigating the relationships between diverse physical phenomena, and who here found one of the first connections between magnetism and light (long before Maxwell postulated that light could be described as the motion of an electromagnetic wave: we shall return to these matters in more detail later). The rotation stops immediately the magnetic field is switched off and is proportional to the distance travelled and to the magnetic field strength.

A remarkable difference between the natural ability of quartz and sugar solutions to turn the plane of polarisation and the Faraday effect is the following. In a material exhibiting natural rotation, for example to the right, the plane of the oscillation a is changed in traversing the material to the plane a', which is an anti-clockwise rotation for the observer looking into the beam. If we reflect the beam and make it pass along through the light-rotating medium, then a' arrives at a''. For an observer looking into the reflected beam, the second rotation to the left exactly cancels the previous one (see figure 95). For a material which shows the Faraday effect the rotation of the plane of polarisation is independent of the direction in which the light travels through the material, so that upon reflection at a mirror the rotation is seen to double (see figure 96, where H shows the direction of the magnetic field lines). The Faraday effect allows one to

Figures 95 and 96. *Top* the direction of rotation of the plane of polarisation in an optically active medium is not reversed with the direction of motion of the light, if in each case one looks in the direction facing the oncoming light. *Bottom* In the case of the Faraday effect, the direction of rotation changes if one looks into the light, but is unchanged if one looks in the direction of the magnetic field.

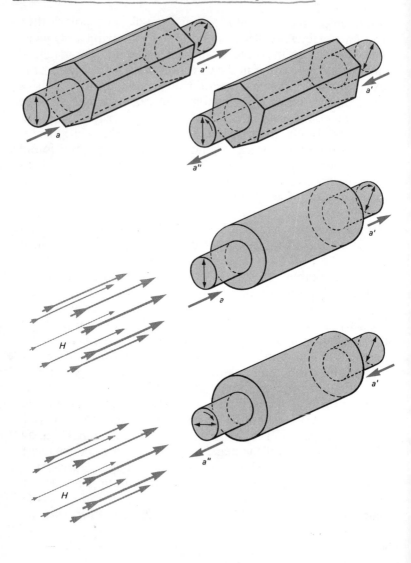

analyse mixtures of hydrocarbons, since each has its own characteristic magnetic rotation ability. Another effect which can be mentioned here is the *Kerr effect*. In an electric field many isotropic materials become anisotropic and uni-axial with the axis in the direction of the electric field lines. The effect is proportional to the square of the electric field. In some liquids the effect follows the electric field so rapidly that it can be used as a light shutter. A related influence of the electric field on optical properties of a material can be seen in ammonium-dihydrophosphate (ADP) which is uni-axial but which, under the influence of an electric field, becomes bi-axial. In the direction of the optical axis it is, under normal circumstances, dark between two crossed polarisers. If an electric potential difference of 10,000 volts is applied between the end surfaces of the crystal, light is transmitted in that direction. The shutter times which one can obtain by applying a pulsed voltage lie in the region of one ten-millionths of a second.

6 Production and detection

34 Light sources

Let us now look at the light sources which are used in optical studies. To start with, for his daily work the optician needs ordinary daylight: direct sunlight, light from the sky or, when that is clouded over, light which filters through the clouds. When the sun parts company with him and the evening red colours the sky again (see section 27) then he, just as any other man, needs artificial lighting. Where in earlier days he used a candle or a floating oilwick, or a paraffin lamp, or gaslight, he uses today the electric bulb, or the fluorescent tube, while on the street and in the factories the sodium- and mercury-lamps are used for lighting.

For his experiments he needs quite different ammunition: gas-discharge lamps, the electric arc and the electric spark discharge, in order to force the atoms to emit their spectral lines. To obtain large amounts of light he has Xenon lamps which are gas-discharge lamps filled with Xenon gas emitting large amounts of almost white light, and high-pressure mercury lamps, in which the discharge proceeds in mercury vapour at a hundred or more atmospheres; these also give off enormous amounts of light.

Confident that the optician chooses the right light sources for his experiments, we ask ourselves what he, as non-optician, as ordinary citizen, requires in the way of artificial light at home, and on the street. Everybody has heard talk of candle power and some have heard of decalumens. What these words mean can only be made clear if we first introduce and explain the concept of solid angle.

Let us imagine a light source at P (figure 97), which is screened off such that it emits light only in the cone C, after which the screen is partially removed so that light shines in

the wider cone D. We then can say that in the second case the apparatus, light-source-plus-screen, gives out more light. The width of the cone determines in part how much light is emitted. To measure the width of the cone we imagine a sphere with P as centre and so large a radius r that the size of the light source and the screen can be assumed to be negligibly small in comparison (figure 98). The cone cuts out of the sphere a piece whose surface area O is a measure for the width of the cone. If we make the radius of the sphere twice as large then the area becomes four times larger. The area of the piece O cut out of the surface of the sphere divided by r^2 is no longer dependent on the size of r. Well now, O/r^2 is called the *solid angle*. If the cone has an irregular shape, such as in figure 99, the area of the surface cut out divided by the square of the radius remains (for sufficiently large r) a measure of the solid angle.

The amount of light emitted is larger in the case of the wider cone of figure 97 (other things being equal), than for the narrower cone. The amount of emitted light is proportional to the solid angle. We now compare two cases where the solid angle is the same, but the area of the emitter is x times as large in the second case as in the first one. The amount of light emitted is then also x times larger. The amount of emitted light, the light current or *flux*, is proportional to the area of the emitter and to the solid angle. If we call the light flux L the surface area of the emitter S, and the solid angle O, then

$$L = BSO.$$

In this equation B is the constant of proportionality, to which the name *brightness* is given. Many emitters have the property that, in whichever direction they radiate, they have

Figures 97, 98, 99 and 100 *Top left* Two light cones.
Top right The concept of a solid angle.
Bottom left An irregularly shaped cone.
Bottom right Emission from the surface *S* in two
different directions.

155

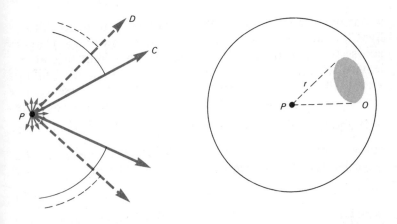

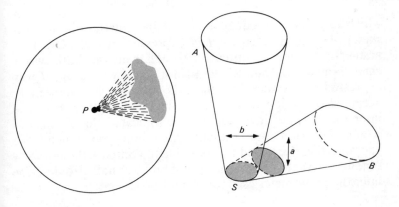

about the same brightness. If we imagine, as in figure 100, a light flux at A leaving the surface S, and spreading straight across the solid angle O, and then another light flux at B, leaving an equally large surface, but at an angle, and filling an equally large solid angle O, then the transverse cross-sectional area of the cone at B is smaller than that of the cone at A and the light flux $L' = BSO. \frac{a}{b}$. (For those familiar with trigonometry we may write $L' = BSO \cos a$, where a is the angle between the perpendicular to the surface and the axis of the skew cone). The ratio $\frac{a}{b}$ is a measure of the skewness with which the light is emitted. For radiation perpendicular to the surface $\frac{a}{b} = 1$; for very skew emission $\frac{a}{b}$ approaches zero.

In simple terms, a light source emitting as much light as another but in a smaller solid angle is 'stronger' or 'more intense'. The light flux divided by the solid angle, $\frac{L}{O}$ is the *light intensity* (we ignore here for simplicity the factor $\frac{a}{b}$ which is practically equal to one if the emission is not too skew). The light intensity I is expressed in *candelas*. This name for the unit of intensity comes from the Latin word *candela* meaning 'candle'. Until not so very long ago I was expressed in candles but there is now an internationally accepted definition of the unit, which we shall give a little later on, because it is rather a complicated definition and would interrupt our present discussion too much. We suppose, therefore, that it is possible to compare the intensity of lamps with that of a defined unit and we shall also describe later the photometer used for this purpose.

A glowing grain A sends out equal amounts of light in all directions. The total flux of light L spreads itself evenly over a solid angle of 4π; the surface of the whole sphere with A as centre divided by the square of the radius of the sphere is after all equal to 4π. The light intensity I is, therefore,

$$I = \frac{L}{O} = \frac{L}{4\pi}$$

If a light source had a light intensity I, which was the same in all directions, then the light flux L would equal $4\pi I$, that is about $12 \cdot 5I$. The light flux is expressed in *lumens*. The older among our readers will remember the term *decalumen*, which at one time was used as the unit to express the flux of the light emitted by lamps. In the case of an ordinary lamp the light intensity is different in different directions. It is zero in the direction of the holder and in other directions the light intensity has a particular value. This is indicated with a thick line around the lamp in figure 101. The partition of the light intensity in different directions can be altered with a reflector (see figure 102 where the partition of the light for the lamp plus the reflector is given). An extreme case is that of a lighthouse light (figure 103). The light shining towards the right from the lamp L is brought together into an approximately parallel beam B by the special circular lens R. The light emitted to the left of the lamp is reflected to the right by a mirror, goes through the lamp and also reaches the lens R, so that it also forms part of the beam B. The light intensity in this beam is thus increased enormously at the cost of that in all other directions. It is possible in this way to obtain light intensities of millions of candelas. By turning the whole set-up about a vertical axis one gives ships in all horizontal directions the possibility of seeing the lighthouse at large

Figures 101, 102, 103 and 104. *Top* Light distribution
from a lamp without and with a reflector.
Middle. A lighthouse light. *Bottom* An increase in
the size of the source gives more light in other
directions but not more in the same direction.

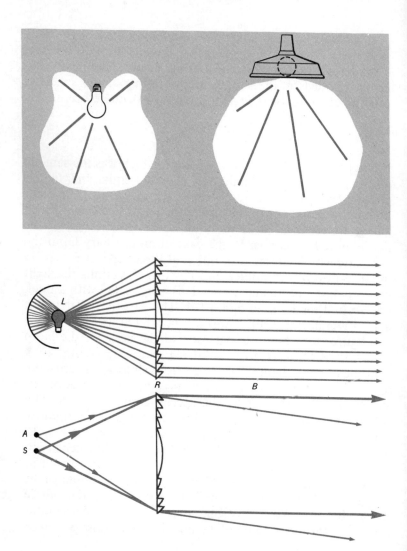

distances for the short time that the beam takes to sweep across the eye of the observer. One might for a moment think that the light intensity could be made larger by making the surface S of the emitter larger. Of course, the total flux would increase since this is proportional to S, but it is in this case easy to see that the light intensity of the beam would not increase. In figure 104 it can be seen that the addition of A to S gives a beam in another direction.

35 Brightness: total radiation

Let us now examine a little more closely the factor B, the brightness. Ignoring again the fraction $\frac{a}{b}$ in order to make the discussion easier, we can write B as

$$B = L/SO$$

in words: the brightness equals the light flux divided by the surface area of the emitter and by the solid angle. A light flux of given area which provides many lumens in a given solid angle is considered to be a useful light source. In order to obtain much light one must strive towards a large brightness.

When a solid body is heated, it emits light and all the more so the higher the temperature. At 600°C the electric iron which one has forgotten to switch off, and the dried out kettle which has been allowed to stay on the hot plate, give off visible light. The tungsten wire in the electric bulb, heated by the electric current passing through it, gives off much more light per unit surface and per unit solid angle: its brightness is much larger; furthermore the light it emits is whiter. The unit of brightness is the *stilb* (from the Greek word *stilbein* meaning 'to shine'). If a surface of one square metre emits one lumen per unit solid angle, then its brightness is one stilb. Put another way: if a surface of area b m² emits so much light in a given direction that the intensity is a candelas, then the brightness is a/b stilb.

A few examples can make clearer the concept of brightness. The flame of a candle has a brightness of one stilb (it is the small particles of soot, heated by the flame, which emit the light). The filament of an electric lamp has a brightness of 200 – 1000 stilb, depending on its size. The matt envelope of the lamp, considered itself as a light source, has a brightness of about 2 stilb. The surface of the sun, whose temperature is about 5600°C has a brightness of 150,000 stilb. It is easy to see that the hotter you make it the more light you get. And that is why the metal tungsten is used for the filament of an electric lamp; it is the metal with the highest melting point. The filament must be metallic in order to conduct the electric current which causes the heating. We can also list the brightness of some gas discharge lamps. The brightness of a sodium light used for street lighting is 5 stilb. That of a super high pressure mercury lamp is 30,000 stilb. The brightness of a fluorescent tube is approximately one stilb.

The light emission from a glowing solid body, a liquid (for example molten steel) or a gas (the sun and other stars) follows certain laws. Light of all wavelengths is emitted: the spectrum is continuous. The total amount of emitted radiation is proportional to the fourth power of the absolute temperature (that is the temperature in degrees Centigrade plus 273), but the distribution of the radiation over the different wavelengths is also very strongly dependent on the temperature. In figure 105 we have shown this partition graphically for a few temperatures, respectively 1000°, 1260°, 1450° and 1650° absolute. The total radiation emitted and its

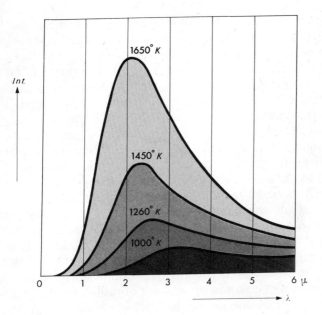

Figure 105. The spectral energy distribution of a black body.

distribution also vary with the nature of the emitter.

The many peculiarities of light emission are much simplified if the radiation occurs under certain special circumstances. This is so remarkable and of such great importance that we shall go into it at greater length. The sides of a hollow space are heated up from the outside in such a way that all parts of the wall have the same temperature. When a particular temperature is reached, and the walls are kept at this temperature by providing the right quantity of heat, each part of the wall emits light but is also illuminated by the other parts. Of the radiation falling upon it, part is reflected and the rest is absorbed and transformed into heat. An equilibrium is produced. The amount of radiation energy per unit volume reaches a particular value which can be shown to be completely independent of the nature of the walls (material, roughness, reflection properties). The distribution of the radiation energy over different wavelengths is also independent of the nature of the walls. Both factors depend only on the temperature of the walls. It is precisely this distribution which is shown in figure 105. This figure gives the distribution for what one calls a *total emitter*. One also speaks of a *black body*, because the distribution of the radiation is the same as that obtained at the same temperature from a body which is black for all wavelengths, i.e. which absorbs radiation of all wavelengths completely. In reality such a body does not exist. We want to make it quite clear that the space filled with radiation is not just a useful figment of the imagination but can indeed be used for measurements. We have only to think that one can make a small opening in the wall, large enough to allow an amount of radiation to escape, sufficient for measurements, but yet so small, that the radiation equilibrium is not noticeably disturbed.

We are now in a position to give the definition of the candela. A black-body radiator of 1 cm^2 surface area has a light intensity of 60 candelas, if the temperature of the black body is that of melting platinum. A pure material has a fixed melting point. One, therefore, need only put some pure platinum into the space inside the total emitter; at the instant that the platinum melts the light intensity is known by definition. This can be compared with that of lamps which can then be used as subsidiary standards. Since the light intensity of an electric lamp is reduced in time (among other reasons by the blackening of the envelope due to the evaporation of small pieces of tungsten from the filament), these lamps are only used now and then to calibrate other lamps which, in their turn, serve as standards. We will later mention a little more about the comparison of light intensities.

The total emitter is also of great importance because the theory of black-body radiation (see section 49) can predict precisely the energy distribution in its spectrum. By comparing the spectrum of an arbitrary light source with that of a black body, one can determine the energy distribution of the light source. Before leaving the subject of black bodies we will mention one more thing. The maximum of the energy in the spectrum moves to shorter wavelengths as the temperature is increased. The wavelength in nm of the maximum is equal to the number 2,893,000 divided by the absolute temperature. Only at such high temperatures as those occurring at the surface of the sun does the maximum lie in the visible region. The wavelength region for which the eye is most sensitive lies precisely at this maximum: the eye is adapted to the spectral energy distribution of sunlight. At a temperature of 2400°C, which the tungsten filament can have in a lamp, the maximum radiation is in the infra-red and only a small part of all radiation, about 4 per cent, falls in the visible region. Furthermore the visible radiation in the red part of the spectrum is more intense than that in the blue-violet part. The light from electric lamps contains more red than occurs in the spectral energy distribution of daylight.

36 Lighting intensity: photometry

We now go over to a new concept which, in practice is a very useful one: the *lighting intensity*. In figure 106 a surface of area S' is drawn on which falls a light flux L'. The amount of light per unit surface area, thus the number of lumens per m², is then L'/S'. The unit for this quantity is called a *lux*. One lux is one lumen per m². The lighting intensity must exceed certain minimum values for one to find the light agreeable and pleasant. Too large a lighting intensity is, on the other hand, also uncomfortable and can sometimes even be harmful. A few numbers will serve as examples. In corridors and such-like 20 lux are enough, in a living room an average of 200 lux for the lighting intensity is enough, except when one reads. It is more pleasant to have 500 lux on one's book. For fine instrument work it is better to have 1,000 lux shining on the work. For sewing of dark materials, and for a drawing board, 2,000 lux are considered necessary. The lighting due to the unencumbered and unclouded sky is large and can (on a horizontal surface) reach 2,000 lux. Direct sunlight on white paper is too strong to be considered comfortable; the lighting intensity can run up to 80,000 lux.

If we take a light source p (figure 107), then at a distance of r metres a surface of one m² will receive a certain number of lumens in a solid angle $1/r^2$. The light flux divided by the solid angle is equal to the light intensity of p in this direction. If we set the surface receiving the light b times further then the solid angle is b^2 times smaller as is the light flux in this solid angle. The lighting intensity is also b^2 times smaller. By varying the distance of a light source from the surface it is illuminating one can, therefore, regulate the lighting intensity. On this fact turns the possibility of comparing light intensities of different sources. This is one of the uses of photometry. The eye is capable of determining whether two adjacent objects have the same brightness. It is, on the other hand, quite impossible to say simply by looking at the surfaces 'this surface is so many times brighter than that surface'.

Figures 106 and 107. *Top* The concept of lighting intensity. *Bottom* A larger solid angle gives greater lighting intensity.

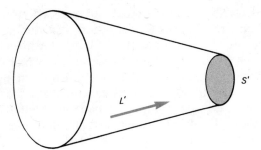

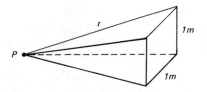

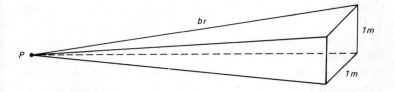

We shall now describe a photometer (developed by Lummer and Brodhun) which uses the variation of distance to measure light intensities. To begin with, the lamp P, whose light intensity is to be determined, and the lamp M, which serves as standard, are mounted, as shown in figure 108, on a rail along which they can be moved. Between them on the rail there is a small plate Q, whose surface is made matt white with magnesium oxide. To do this it is held in the white vapour of burning magnesium. By adjusting the distance of the lamps from Q both sides are equally lit. How that condition is observed we shall describe later but supposing for now that it can be, we can then understand from what was said earlier that the ratio of the light intensities of P and M is equal to the square of the ratio of the distances to the plate. Even if we look at an angle at such a perfectly matt white surface, we can still observe its brightness. A perfectly matt surface has the same brightness from whatever angle it is observed. Use is made of this fact (figure 109).

Two mirrors are mounted in a box, so that each receives light from one side of the plate Q. A prism combination of special form is placed where the two reflected beams cross each other. A is a glass prism such as was earlier illustrated in figure 15. The beam falling on it from top right is totally reflected to bottom right by the slanting side of A. B is a prism of approximately the same shape. Its slanting side is not, however, so simple, for around its middle part it is rounded off. The flat middle part is glued with transparent cement to the slanting side of A. The light falling on to B from top left is reflected to bottom left by the rounded part of its slanting side. The middle part of the beam, however, goes right through the cemented part and travels unhindered to the bottom right. When we said just now that the light falling

Figures 108 and 109. *Top* The two sides
of the plate *Q* are illuminated by the
lamp *P* and the standard lamp *M*.
Bottom Comparison of lighting intensities
according to Lummer and Brodhun.

167

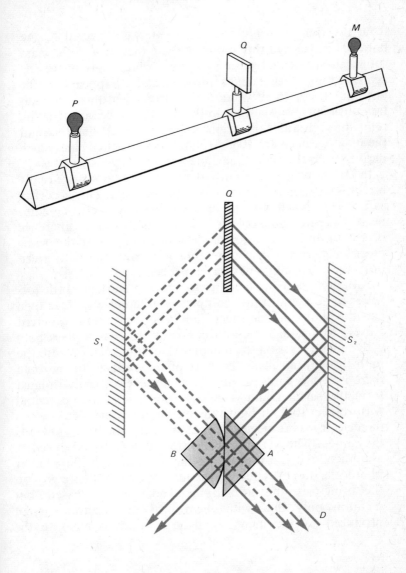

from the right upper corner on to A was reflected to the bottom right corner this applied only to that part of the beam round the cemented piece. The part which falls on to the cemented piece goes right through and disappears in the bottom left corner. If we now look from D at this combination of prisms, we shall see in the middle the beam travelling right through and this originates from the left-hand side of the plate Q, in figure 108. Around it we see the beam which derives from the right-hand side.

In this way it is possible to make the two sides equally bright with an accuracy of about one per cent. This accuracy can only be reached if the light sources that are to be compared have the same colour. As soon as there is a difference in colour our eye unfortunately no longer has the same precision, and if for example one compares red with green light, the uncertainty may be ten per cent.

Although there are facilities to improve matters a little it is better to go about it in a completely different way. One then uses the photo-electric effect. This crops up in many different guises. A so-called vacuum cell is an evacuated glass bulb with a metal layer on the inner surface. Light can fall into the bulb through an uncoated part of the surface. In the bulb there is also a wire, the anode, which is electrically isolated from the surface, and is given a positive electric potential with respect to it. If light falls on the inner metallic coating then electrons are ejected from it and they are drawn towards the anode. The very weak electric current so produced is amplified, and is a measure of the infalling light flux. Other photocells do not require a vacuum. We cannot here go into the principles upon which their operation is based, but mention only that with them also the electric current produced by the incoming light is used to measure the lighting intensity.

Great difficulty with the use of photocells comes from the fact that their 'sensitivity' is a strong function of the wavelength of the light falling upon them and, therefore, of the spectral energy distribution of the light to be measured. It has proved worth the trouble to measure the spectral sensitivity. There are methods worked out for this and much photometric work is now performed with the help of photocells. By careful work the accuracy can be made even better than that of the eye. Fatigue of the observer, which is an obstacle in visual photometry, disappears. This all makes it understandable that the objective photometry with photocells has developed greatly. The light meters of cameras are also photocells, which measure the lighting intensity. They are, therefore, lux-meters even though they do not give the lighting intensity in lux. Their reading is combined with the film speed and lens opening so that they can give us the correct value of the shutter speed required. For in taking photographs one must consider the exposure which is the product of the lighting intensity and the time of exposure. The exposure is the decisive quantity which determines whether the correct amount of light energy has fallen upon the film so that after development the required blackening and possibly colouring is obtained in the picture. If the exposure is right for a given lens opening, then a longer exposure time will be needed for a narrower lens opening. Since the lighting intensity on the film is proportional to the solid angle of the illuminating beam, it is also proportional to the open surface of the lens. If the diameter of this is halved then the open area is made four times smaller which makes it necessary to increase the time of exposure by a factor of four.

37 The human eye

In the preceding sections we have discussed the production and detection of light. In connection with this we now wish to describe the most important optical detection instrument, the eye. Man relies more on his eye than does the dog, for whom smell, sound and hearing are of overwhelming importance. There is so much to say about our eyes, because there has been so much research and so much thought on this subject, that it is impossible to do justice to it all in a short piece. The reader is referred to R. L. Gregory's *Eye and Brain*, another volume which has already appeared in the series to which this book belongs, and which deals exclusively with the eye and with vision. We restrict ourselves here to a short description of the human eye as an optical instrument.

Yet vision is very pertinent to our enquiry. If someone asks himself 'What is light?', then he could easily think that the answer should go roughly, 'Well, what you see, that is light'. On closer examination this answer holds no water, as we hope to make clear in a short while.

In figure 110 we have given a schematic cross-section of the eye. More precisely: the right eye is halved by a horizontal cut, and the figure shows how the bottom half appears. The eyeball, filled with a jelly-like mass, is surrounded by a strong envelope, covered on the inside by a membrane which does not allow much light through. The front part bulges out somewhat and is very clearly transparent. This is where the light comes in, but not all this light reaches the back of the eyeball where the light-sensitive cells are placed. After it has travelled through the transparent cap, the cornea, and through the water-like fluid which follows it, the light reaches a circular screen with a round opening. The screen

Figure 110. The eye as a detector.   171

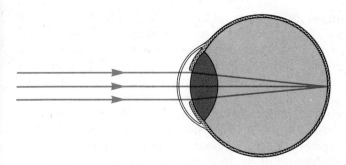

stops the light from going through the coloured cells of which it is composed. The round opening in the middle (the pupil) transmits the light, which then passes through the lens of the eye, traverses the vitreous body (the above-mentioned jelly-like mass) and so reaches the back surface. The arched cornea and the lens of the eye together form the image-making optics. They form the image on the retina. The diaphragm with the round opening regulates the quantity of light which takes part in the image formation. In daylight the diameter of the pupil is about 2 mm whereas in very weak light it widens itself to 8 mm or more. Seen from the front the pupil looks like a black disc. That is because it is dark behind it. It is as if one looked at the narrow opening of a closed box. The screen can have different colours, depending on the colour of the cells which lie immediately in front of those darker cells which stop the light. It is, therefore, called the iris (the Latin name for rainbow).

The human eye (and also the eye of many animals) can therefore, be compared to a camera. There is even a possibility of focusing: in order to sharpen up the images of close lying objects the lens is made rounder by a ring of muscles.

Figure 111. What happens
behind the retina, according to Descartes.

Unfortunately, the ability to do this is lost with the passage of years. The older amongst us must then make use of an auxiliary lens, the reading spectacle. The field of view is small, corresponding to 1 cm at a distance of 1·7 m, at least if one only takes account of that part of the field of vision where good focus can be obtained. Because of the supple movement possibilities, with the help of half a dozen muscles, one is not too worried about how small this 'sharp' field of view is; the eye can fix itself on any point so fast that one is quite unconscious of the movement. In relation to the size of the cells in the retina, the 'sharpness of observation' of a good eye is about one minute of arc, that is 0·5 mm at a distance of 1·7 m.

Around the region of sharp visibility the retina is also sensitive to light, even though it is not able to distinguish details so well. The 'diffused' field of view is rather large: while one looks straight out one can still vaguely see the tip of one's nose. How then does the eye 'work'? The correct and most complete answer is that we do not know. We have all sorts of theories and we do know the workings of many links in the chain. Thus it is known that in the cells of the retina there is a very small amount of light-sensitive material. If light falls on the cell several chemical changes occur in this material which generate a number of small electrical impulses along the nerve fibre connected to the cell. These signals are then transmitted to a particular part of the the brain. What happens then who can possibly tell? How do the nerves and the brain cells transform and recreate the images formed on the retina? We are for example trained to interpret the images formed upside down on the retina as being the right way up. There must be something there which corresponds to a computer which takes in data, selects and

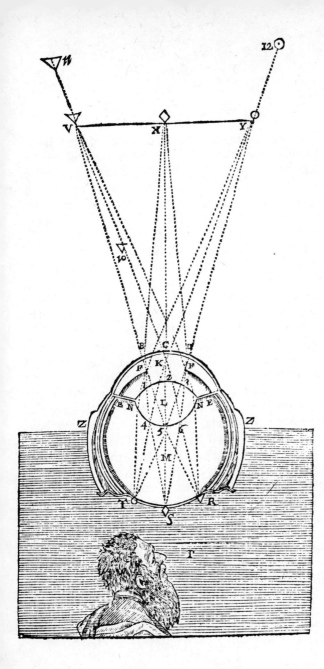

compares them with others and makes calculations. If we remember further that the two eyes of a person receive images which are a little bit different from each other (because they are placed at different positions in space and, therefore, have a different perspective) and that it is precisely these differences which help us to see in depth, then we really begin to be dazzled. 'Behind' or rather 'past' the retina a great deal happens. Descartes put this in a picture which is reproduced in figure 111: the soul or the mind of the observer sits 'behind' the retina. In short: the eye is a camera with photocells and a computer. The physicist has no knowledge of what sits behind this to produce a perception. This is a good point at which to emphasize that a beam of light itself is invisible. For we imagine we can see the light energy which moves past us in the form of a beam when small bits of dust blow into it. But what then is really the case? The beam hits the pieces of dust, which scatter the light, and of this scattered light part reaches the eye. So we do see the path along which the beam travels, but not the light of the beam itself. Let us investigate what happens if the light beam falls *on the eye*. In so far as it reaches the retina, the energy falling on the retina is changed into chemical and electrical energy. There then occurs the mysterious process of the formation of a light impression; the energy of the light has then disappeared. As soon as you see light, it disappears. With a continuous flux of light part of the energy is absorbed and changed into light impressions. One then gets the feeling that one sees light continuously, as long as the absorbed part of the light flux signals: 'there is radiant energy here in the form of light'. What then is light? The light impression, the awareness of seeing light? But this awareness can also be awakened by mechanical pressure, by electrical currents or by drunkenness. One can almost say that physicists call light that imagined model of the motion of waves in space with which they try to bring together the various phenomena under a unified system and thus to 'explain' them.

We have not quite reached this point, if we remember that when discussing the interaction of the light flux and the molecules in the light sensitive material of the retina cell, account must be taken of the particle-like character which must be ascribed to the radiation (see sections 50 and 52).

38 A backward glance

We stop here for a moment and ask ourselves to what extent we have answered the question 'what is light'? Our working hypothesis: 'light is a wave-motion', has given us the explanation of so many phenomena that we have accepted it as a proper theory of light. In so far as a physicist may use this word: light *is* a wave motion, and a transversal one at that. We have studied the refraction and the reflection of these light waves and have found applications in lenses, mirrors and prisms; we have discussed the methods by which the speed of light is measured; the wavelength and phase of the waves manifested themselves in interference and diffraction; the transversal character of the oscillations emerged clearly from the phenomena of polarisation; and finally we gave an overall description of the ways whereby the intensity of light is produced and measured – in this connection we also discussed the structure of the eye. In all this we have been careful to avoid the questions of how light is created and of what occurs in light sources; we also used photocells to measure light quantities without discussing how the light is changed into electrical current in them. The investigation of this new group of problems will open our eyes to a whole new series of properties of light and matter. But even for the properties we have already discussed we have now and then passed over something or other which, at the time, it was not convenient to discuss, but about which we shall have to speak in order to make our description of the character of the light oscillations as full as possible. In discussing refraction and reflection of light at the interface between two media we said nothing about the relative intensities of the refracted and reflected rays. We gave no explanation for the difference in the speed of light *in vacuo* from that in different transparent media; for that matter we did not go into the question of the why and wherefore of this transparency. We have also to look for a 'carrier' of the light waves: waves cannot stand on their own, there must be something that waves. In the remainder of this book we shall try to give as good an answer as possible to all these questions: we start with the last one on our list.

7 Electromagnetic field

39 The Aether

Just as water-waves travel in water, so also must light waves travel in 'something'. So argued the physicists of the last century and of the beginning of this century. They therefore tried to discover the properties of this carrier material, which they called 'aether'. We cannot see the aether wave, as we can water; we can, however, imagine the aether as a material which permeates everything, unnoticed by our senses, but whose oscillations become noticeable as light. Water is there, even when there are no waves on it; is the aether also there, when it is dark? Right from the start one could say that the answer to this last question would be difficult to give; even if the existence of the aether can be assumed, it remains a dubious matter – the physicist prefers to occupy himself with more tangible problems. Nevertheless, all the physicists of the period continued to try to discover the properties of this mysterious matter.

Fresnel, whom we have already met earlier in our tale (when we discussed diffraction effects), supposed that the aether must have about the same elastic properties as all isotropic matter. And it looked for a time as if he were right. With this theory Fresnel seemed able to solve the problem of the reflection of polarised light at the interface between two media. The experiment shows that whenever a plane wave hits the interface between two materials at a particular angle, the amounts of light which are reflected and transmitted respectively depend not only on the size of the angle of incidence, and on the refractive indices on each side of the interface, but also on the state of polarisation of the light. If linearly polarised light falls on the interface then the amount of reflected light is a maximum if the direction of oscillation

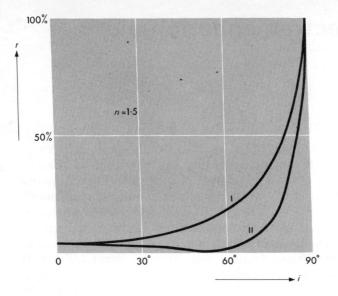

is perpendicular to the plane of incidence (the plane of incidence is the plane defined by the incoming ray and the perpendicular to the reflecting surface) and reaches a minimum if the direction of oscillation lies in the plane of incidence. The amount of reflected light even becomes zero, if the light oscillating in the plane of incidence falls on to the surface at a particular angle. We have already met these phenomena at the beginning of our discussion on the polarisation of light. We call the angle of incidence, for which there is no reflection of light oscillating in the plane of incidence, *Brewster's angle*. Unpolarised light, that is to say light of which the direction of oscillation is not constant, will, if it comes in at this angle, contain upon reflection only those oscillations perpendicular to the plane of incidence. This is one way of producing linearly polarised light, which we already used at the beginning of section 30. We shall not give here the formulae which Fresnel worked out. Instead we sketch in figure 112 a graph showing the coefficient of reflection r for light that is polarised perpendicular to ($\perp$) and

Figures 112 and 113. *Left* Reflection
of polarised light at a glass surface.
The refractive index of the glass is 1 5.
Below Fizeau's experiment to determine
the speed of light in flowing water.

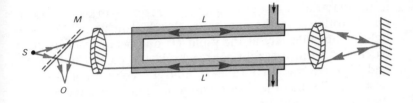

parallel to ($=$) the plane of incidence. The values given are
those for the case when the ratio of the refractive indices on
either side of the interface equals 2/3. This result was a
beautiful success for the theory of the aether. But overwhelming difficulties can be brought against this hypothesis of an
elastic aether. We know that light oscillations are transversal.
Well now, transversal oscillations are only to be expected
in solid materials. The aether should, therefore, be a solid.
But in a solid material longitudinal oscillations can also
arise and these would certainly come into being at an
interface even if the incoming beam were purely transversal.
One therefore has to bring in an extra hypothesis about the
aether to explain away the lack of these longitudinal oscillations. This aether must, therefore, be a quite uncommon
material: a solid material which we do not notice when we go
through it, and whose elastic behaviour is unique.

40 Moving media

Another idea of Fresnel's was: if one moves relative to the
aether (assuming that it exists) then the speed of light must be
increased by the speed of the relative motion. Thus the speed
of light in a material which moves with a speed u against the
direction of motion of the light becomes ($v + u$), if the speed

in the material at rest was equal to v. Fizeau worked this idea out as follows. In the apparatus sketched in figure 113 two light beams interfere at the point O: one beam has travelled clockwise from the light source S via the partial mirror M and through the two tubes L and L' containing flowing liquid, while the other beam has gone along the same path in an anti-clockwise direction. If one increases the speed of the flowing liquid through the tubes then the interference bands formed at O should displace themselves a little: because the speed of light in the two paths is different (in the one case $(v + u)$ and in the other $(v - u)$ the phaselength (the number of wavelengths included in the path) also depends on the direction along which the path is followed. The difference in phaselength determines the position of the interference bands: this difference becomes larger as the speed of the liquid in the tubes is increased. The outcome of the experiment was, however, quite different from that expected. Instead of the speed $w = v + u$, Fizeau's experiments gave a result which proved to be dependent on the refractive index of the liquid used:

$$w = v + u \left(1 - \frac{1}{n^2}\right)$$

The only reason that one could think of to explain this result was that the aether was swept with the liquid although not completely but with a 'drag coefficient' $\left(1 - \frac{1}{n^2}\right)$. We shall not ask ourselves here how this explanation is reached; it would only lead to our confusion. It is, however, interesting to continue our questions in this direction, now that we have noticed that the theory of the aether leads to difficulties. And so we ask ourselves: if the aether reaches throughout space, does not our earth move with respect to it? Then there should be a noticeable difference in the speed of light along, and perpendicular to, the direction of motion of the earth, because of the aether wind which blows unnoticed in our ears and eyes. Let the speed of the earth be u. From the point of view of the aether, a distance l in the direction of the motion of the earth is covered by light in a time $\dfrac{l}{c-u}$ and on the way back in a time $\dfrac{l}{c+u}$. In a direction perpendicular to this the same distance is covered both there and back in a time $\dfrac{l}{\sqrt{c^2-u^2}}$. There is, therefore, a difference in the time needed to cover the same distance: in the direction of motion of the earth the time taken is

$$\frac{2cl}{c^2-u^2},$$

and perpendicularly to this it is (see figure 114)

$$\frac{2l}{\sqrt{c^2-u^2}}.$$

To measure this difference Michelson and Morley performed in 1887 a famous experiment using the interferometer which we discussed previously in section 21. In this apparatus the incoming light beam is split by the partial mirror S (see figure 115) into two beams which follow mutually perpendicular paths and finally interfere at P. Parallel light is used and the distances SM_1 and SM_2 are made approximately equal; it is also necessary to ensure that the mirrors M_1 and M_2 make a small angle with each other so that the interference lines in the plane of the drawing become visible at P.

This situation is just made for the measurement of the aether wind (see above). If the interferometer is first placed so that one leg points in the direction of the aether wind, and we then turn the whole apparatus in the plane of the drawing through 90° then the positions of the two legs relative to the aether wind are interchanged. The original difference in travel time between the two paths is then changed into its opposite. The result should be that the interference pattern should be slightly shifted. When the experiment was performed nothing of this was noticed. But the expected effect was also very small. The speed of the earth about the sun is about three hundred-thousandths of the speed of light. According to our discussion above we can expect a difference in the time of travel for equal distances of $\frac{2l}{c} \cdot \frac{1}{2} \frac{u^2}{c^2}$. The travel time for one of the paths is $\frac{2l}{c}$. The difference is about one thousand-millionths of this. If the light makes a million oscillations in one of the legs on its round trip (this comes about, for red light, when the length of the leg is about 60 cm, since 60 cm is one million times λ when λ equals 600 nm) then a thousanth of an oscillation more or less than this must be made along the other leg. The phase difference is, therefore, in the order of one thousanth, so that the interference pattern is shifted over one thousanth of a line width. One can try and make the observation somewhat easier by increasing the length of the legs. But one then runs into mechanical difficulties: one would like for example to use bars 60 metres long. Michelson and Morley succeeded, with the use of mirrors, in folding the light path in the two legs eight times upon itself and so obtained longer path lengths. But the result still remained the same: no shift in the interference pattern could be observed.

Figures 114 and 115. *Top* Propagation
transverse and parallel to the direction
of motion of the aether. *Bottom* Michelson's
interferometer once again.

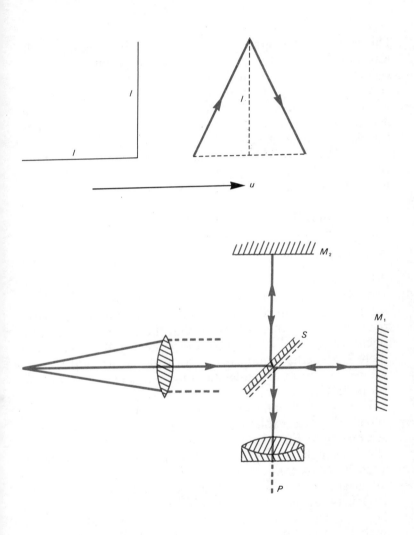

This result is in flagrant conflict with the hypothesis which was put forward to explain Fizeau's experiment. If one performs the experiment in the air, for which the drag co-efficient is equal to zero (the refractive index is almost equal to one) then one expects a displacement, or conversely the negative result points to a drag coefficient of one: the aether travels with the apparatus, there is no aether wind.

We see that all sorts of difficulties arise from the use of the concept of the aether, by which we understand some elastic material through which the light oscillations travel. A brilliant attempt to resolve these difficulties was made by Lorentz and Fitzgerald (1902). If one supposes that all materials shrink because of their motion with a speed u, and that they do so by a fraction $\frac{1}{2}\frac{u^2}{c^2}$ of their length, one can then understand at once why the experiment of Michelson and Morley gave a negative result: the leg of the interferometer which pointed in the direction of motion of the earth relative to the aether shrank so that there was in the end no phase difference as a result of the aether wind. Thus even if there is an aether wind, we cannot detect it. How then shall we ever arrive at an understanding of the existence and the properties of the aether?

Finally, we shall discuss how the results of Fizeau's experiment are explained in the light of this hypothesis. According to Fitzgerald the molecules of the water through which the light is shining should come closer to each other as a result of this contraction, so that the refractive index of the material changes. But we do not yet understand the relationship between intermolecular distance and refractive index. So long as we have not understood how light interacts with the structure of matter we cannot, therefore, explain

Fizeau's experiment with the help of Fitzgerald and Lorentz's hypothesis. We can imagine an experiment which suggests that the contraction of matter is not the only thing that will happen in moving media. The contraction of a medium in the direction of motion brings about the result that the refractive index is no longer the same in all directions: there should appear the phenomenon of uni-laxial double refraction. Rayleigh and Brace made – our story becomes monotonous – vain attempts to measure this effect. It is clear that we shall not get any further in this way: the difficulties are insoluble so long as our understanding of the peculiarities of light is not increased. In the following sections we try to show that the theory of the electromagnetic field, which was developed by James Clark Maxwell (1831–79) gives the required broadening of the wave theory of light.

41 Electric and magnetic fields

The two observations which form the basis of the theory of the electromagnetic field are familiar to us from daily life: an ebony comb which is rubbed with a silk cloth picks up small pieces of paper; a freshly ground pair of scissors does the same with steel pins. One says that the ebony becomes electrically charged; the scissors behave like a magnet. We know also that there are two kinds of electric charge; when we comb our hair with the above-mentioned comb the hairs are attracted by it, but repel each other. We can explain this as follows: the comb, originally uncharged, obtains on contact with the hairs a particular kind of charge; this kind of charge we call negative. The hairs become positively charged. As is known, negative and positive charges attract each other, like charges repel each other. We can also describe the situation in these words: an electric charge gives rise in the space around it to an electric field; another charge which comes into this field feels a force F whose direction lies along the line between the two charges. The field of an electric charge, therefore, has everywhere a direction pointing away from the spot where the charge is (see figure 116). We find something similar with magnets. Each magnet has a 'south pole' and a 'north pole'. Similar poles repel and opposite poles attract each other. A magnet in the magnetic field of another will feel forces which force it into a particular orientation; on this depends the working of the compass. We draw the attention of the reader to an important difference between electric charges and magnets. A body can have positive or negative electric charge; a magnet always has both a north and a south pole. If one breaks a magnet into two, then each half again has a north and a south pole.

It can be shown that an electric current has a magnetic field about it: a coil carrying a current and a magnet have precisely the same effect on another magnet in their surroundings. If one brings a freely rotateable small magnet, for example a compass needle, in the field of a coil, or of a magnet (see figure 117) then it points in the direction of the magnetic field at the spot. In this way we can map the field at all points. Electric charges exert forces upon each other and so do electric currents (or magnets). Now does a magnetic field also influence the existence of an electric field? This question was answered by Michael Faraday in his famous experiments concerned with induction (1831). If a conducting wire (figure 118) is wound round a magnet and the magnet is then suddenly removed from the winding, a pulse of current is created in the conductor provided its ends are connected to each other. The motion of the electricity in the wire is

Figures 116 and 117. *Top* The electric field around a positively charged sphere. *Bottom* The field of a magnet.

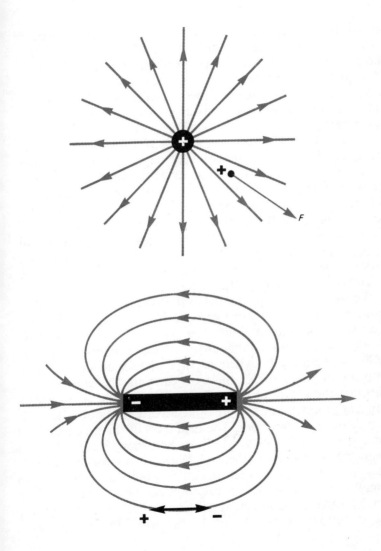

caused by an electric field which is induced in the conductor by the *change* of the magnetic field. The strength of the current can be shown to be proportional to the speed with which the magnet moves.

Maxwell tried to set up a theory which brought together the magnetic and electric fields in a system of equations. To reach his goal he was short of one fact: we said that a change in a magnetic field creates an electric field; what then is the influence of the electric field on the magnetic field? Maxwell assumed that there exists an inductive force analogous to that shown in Faraday's experiment. It takes us too far out of our way to describe here the experiments by which this effect can be demonstrated. But in the following we shall see how the existence of electromagnetic waves depends on the reciprocal symmetry of electric and magnetic fields. The most important proof of the correctness of Maxwell's theory is, therefore, the existence of electromagnetic waves.

We shall use a simple model to try to make it plausible that something like waves must exist in the electromagnetic field. To this end we look at figure 119. An electric current j which flows along a long straight wire causes a magnetic field H whose direction everywhere is perpendicular to the wire and tangent to some circle; the wire carrying the current goes through the centre of these circles. We call the curve whose tangent at any point has the same direction as does the field, a *field line* or a *force line*. The field lines of the magnetic field of a straight current-carrying wire are, therefore, circles in a plane perpendicular to the wire. We now suppose an alternating current to go through the wire; we divide the wire into small pieces and we investigate how the field develops about such a small element. We restrict ourselves for the time being to directions perpendicular to the wire. In the following paragraphs we shall see the connection between the field of such a current element and that of a dipole (section 43) and of a molecular oscillator (section 46). Whenever the current in the wire changes direction the magnetic field changes sign, although the shape of the field lines remains the same. We now have a changing magnetic field, and according to Faraday an electric field is, therefore, induced. We notice the similarity between the geometry of the magnetic field lines in figures 118 and 119: they are closed curves. It is, therefore, plausible that the electric field will behave similarly in both situations: the field lines of the electric field and the magnetic field fit into each other like the links in a chain (see figure 120). This electric field E is again an alternating field. We said that, according to Maxwell, an alternating electric field induces a magnetic field, shown in the figure by the letter H. Because the interaction between the E and the H field is symmetrical, this H field, in its turn, forms a link in the chain with the E field. The new magnetic field H in its turn induces another E field and so the wave spreads itself.

The description we have given here is only an approximate model: for an adequate description of electromagnetic waves a subtle use of mathematical concepts is needed. But nevertheless we now see that the electromagnetic field of a straight wire carrying an alternating current, spreads itself through space in a manner which makes us think of the water waves of our previous descriptions. We point out that two magnitudes play a role here, namely the electric field E and the magnetic field H, and that these are always perpendicular to each other and transverse to the direction of motion of the wave. This last fact we show again in figure 121 which depicts more accurately the real position of the field than did the model in figure 120.

Figures 118, 119, 120 and 121. *Below left* Faraday's induction experiment.
Below right The magnetic field around a straight conducting wire.
Top right Spread of an electromagnetic field from a current element.
Bottom right Propagation of the field at some distance from a current element.
The arrow *S* indicates the direction of propagation.

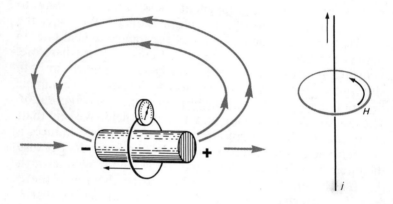

42 Light as an electromagnetic wave

According to Maxwell's theory electromagnetic waves are,
therefore, possible. Another important conclusion can be
drawn from this theory: the speed of propagation of electromagnetic waves *in vacuo* is a constant of nature, and equal to
the speed of light *c*. This does suggest rather strongly that
light is an electromagnetic wave motion. To show that this is
so we can follow three lines of attack, the results of which
strongly support each other. In the first place show that all
the properties of light can be explained by Maxwell's theory.
In the second place show in experiments with electromagnetic

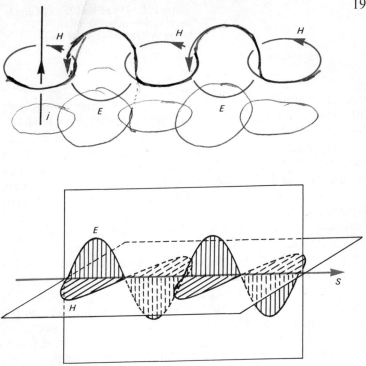

waves that they behave like light. In the third place perform new experiments with light which can only be explained with Maxwell's theory.

As an example of the first method we shall treat the reflection of linearly polarised light at the interface between two media. We have seen that this problem was solved by Fresnel with the theory of an elastic aether, but not without difficulties in connection with the possibility of longitudinal elastic oscillations. It comes out that the phenomenon can be explained with Maxwell's equations without having to assume any additional hypotheses about the existence and

Figures 122, 123 and 124. *Top* The dipole
antenna and a dipole receiver.
Bottom A detector of an *H* field.

properties of an aether. We cannot give the calculations here
but only attempt to make the argument somewhat plausible.
For this we need a description of the behaviour of electromagnetic fields in matter. But we can get along for the time
being by assuming that the *H* field and the *E* field change at
an interface and that they do not do this in the same way.
It is then understandable that the situation is different
depending on whether the *E* field oscillates in the plane of
incidence or perpendicular to this (the *H* field is as we know
always perpendicular to the *E* field). We can also say something about the mathematics of the case, without knowing
the precise form of the equations. The *E* vector has three
spatial components. We suppose that the components of *E* in
the incoming ray are known. We want to know the components in the reflected and the refracted rays, which give us six
unknowns. Now, if we only had the *E* vector at our disposal
we could set up three equations, one for each co-ordinate. We
would then need three other equations in order to be able to
work out all six unknowns. This would force us to put
together additional hypotheses just as Fresnel had to do in his
theory of an elastic aether. But we are saved by the existence
of the *H* field, which gives us three further relations while the
number of unknowns is not increased, since the *H* field and
the *E* field are connected through Maxwell's equations. The
nice thing about this is that in passing the longitudinal
oscillations also disappear. We can, therefore, be very
successful with the theoretical side of the question.

To those who are not fully convinced of the matter we add
that we promised not to give any mathematical descriptions,
but that without these it is only possible to give a rough
outline of Maxwell's theory. For this reason we will allow the
experiments to speak for themselves in the following section.

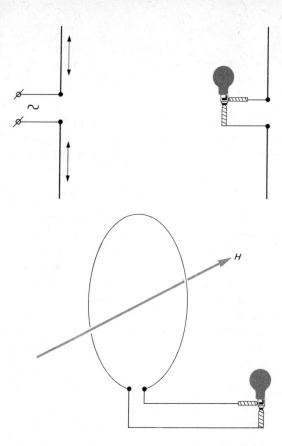

43 Radio waves

We now follow the second approach which we gave to certify the electromagnetic character of light waves: we must show that electromagnetic waves behave like light waves. The first experiments in this direction were done by Heinrich Hertz (1857–94); for many unbelievers they proved a sufficient inducement for accepting Maxwell's theories. Hertz first developed a way of creating strong electromagnetic waves. He fed an alternating potential to the two halves of a straight conductor which was split in the middle (figure 122). For a particular value of the frequency this antenna will resonate: the amplitude of the emitted radiation reaches a maximum value at this frequency. The connection between the wavelength and frequency of the electric waves in and around the conductor is (see section 5) $\lambda = \dfrac{c}{v}$ where c is the speed of propagation and v is the frequency. To each frequency there thus corresponds a given wavelength; if the frequency is so chosen that the wavelength is twice the length of the antenna then standing electric waves are formed along it. Those waves reflected from the end of the antenna interfere constructively with those going towards it. Such an antenna one calls a *dipole*: it consists of two parts which are alternately charged electrically positive and negative. Hertz used a similar dipole as a receiving antenna or detector: this resonates because an antinode is formed at the mid point, and the electric field created there is strong enough to light a lamp (figure 123).

In the previous section we discussed the field emitted by a dipole; we said that the electric component is parallel to the direction of the current in the dipole. We can check this at once with the broadcasting antenna and detector described here. If we place the detector at right angles to the antenna then the lamp does not glow; while when the two are placed parallel it does. It must be remembered that just as the emitting antenna is driven by an electric field, so the detector only reacts to the electric component of the emitted waves. We can build a detector which only sees the magnetic component of the field by taking a loop of copper wire; if the ends are attached to a lamp then this glows when the magnetic field component goes through the loop. We are then again concerned with the induction of an electric field in the conductor as discovered by Faraday (figure 124).

Figure 125. Standing waves on a metal plate. 195

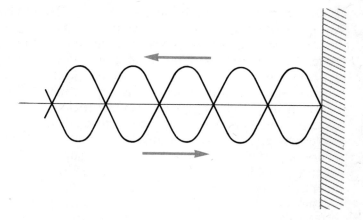

Hertz investigated whether these waves obey Snell's law of reflection by allowing them to be reflected on a metallic plate (several times larger than the wavelength). If he made the angle of incidence equal to zero he observed standing waves, created by the interference of the onfalling and reflected waves (figure 125).* The law of refraction was checked using prisms made of paraffin and water. In agreement with the positive results of these experiments it was shown that a bottle filled with petroleum acted like a cylindrical lens. We could go on in this way; it is, however, already clear enough:

* In 1890, O. Wiener demonstrated the existence of standing waves for visible light. He placed a thin layer of light-sensitive material close to a mirror, at a very slight angle. At the points where the distance from the mirror is an odd number times $\frac{1}{4}\lambda$, an anti-node of the standing wave is expected, and there the light-sensitive material was blackened (see figure 146a for nodes and anti-nodes). It remained unaffected at those points which were an even number times $\frac{1}{4}\lambda$ from the mirror, and where a node of the standing wave was, therefore, expected.

electromagnetic waves do behave like light. In Hertz's time it was extraordinarily difficult to set up experiments such as these; the big stumbling block was the high frequencies needed for the alternating potential. For with a wavelength of 10 cm and c equal to 3.10^{10} cm per second the frequency becomes equal to 3.10^9 oscillations per second. To create such high frequencies Hertz used special tricks. The unit of frequency, oscillations per second, is often called a *Hertz*.

We now give another example of a proof for Maxwell's theory according to the third method we suggested: a new experiment with light waves whose result is predicted by the theory. One knows that a gas kept in a closed space exerts a pressure on the walls of this space. A gas pressure is a measure of the energy of the randomly moving molecules of the gas. It is the same with light: from a consideration of the energetics one can deduce that an electromagnetic wave will exert a pressure on the wall which it meets. It makes a difference whether the wave is absorbed or reflected at the wall; when it is reflected the light pressure is twice as large as when it is absorbed. In a particularly beautiful experiment Lebedew (1901) succeeded in measuring the pressure of light. Its size is under earthly circumstances almost immeasurably small but it does play a role in the processes occurring in stars, which are gigantic sources of radiation.

44 No more Aether

One may, in the meantime, ask oneself, 'What now of the aether?' In our description of Maxwell's theory we have had no need to talk about it; we simply do not need the concept and will, therefore, no longer use it. That which oscillates during light oscillations is the electromagnetic field, and that is a real measurable something. How then do we proceed when faced with experiments such as those of Michelson and Morley and Fizeau, from which it becomes evident that something peculiar does occur in moving media? Maxwell's theory does not help us completely out of the difficulties here. Already in 1905 Einstein showed that Maxwell's equations are no longer symmetrical when moving media are involved. He provided the example of a conductor in the field of a magnet. Let us imagine first that the magnet is moving. Where the conductor is, the magnetic field is changing and this, as we said in section 41, induces an electric field there. This electric field causes the charges in the conductor to move.

Now when we imagine the conductor to be moving the same charge currents develop in it because, from the experimental point of view, the situation has not been changed. Yet there is no electric field created in the surroundings of the magnet. We make clear the paradox and point a way to its solution by imagining that we hold the magnet in the left hand and the conductor in the right. What does it matter which hand we move? This consideration, and Michelson and Morley's experiment, point in the same direction; an aether, that is to say a medium in *absolute* rest, does not exist.

Physical phenomena depend only on the *relative* motions of the media. This hypothesis forms the famous principle of relativity of Einstein's. With this hypothesis as guiding line and earlier investigations of Lorenz and Poincaré as backbone, Einstein developed his theory of relativity. The most important conclusion of this theory is that the speed of light *in vacuo* is independent of the state of motion of the light source. Together with his principle of relativity this gives a complete explanation of the negative results of the experiment of Michelson and Morley. A further consequence of

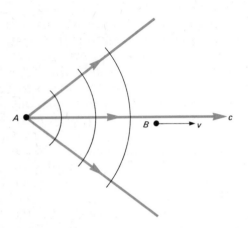

Einstein's theory of relativity is that a moving observer measures exactly the same speed of light as one standing still (see figure 126 where B is the observer and A is the light source). Thus however fast one is going, one cannot catch up with the light: c is the largest speed with which a physical happening can propagate itself in our universe.

Certain formulae of Lorentz which also follow from the theory of relativity put us in a position to calculate how time and space in a co-ordinate system x,y,z (see figure 127) appear to an observer W moving relative to this co-ordinate system. These formulae do not agree with the laws of motion which Galileo developed intuitively, and which were further developed by Newton, who went to work in a somewhat more critical manner. This circumstance, together with other consequences mentioned above, led to a great deal of opposition to Einstein's theory. Had not as great a philosopher as Kant stated that the concepts of 'time' and 'space' such as these were formulated by Galileo were given man-

Figure 127. An observer *W* moves relative to a co-ordinate system, *X, Y, Z*.

199

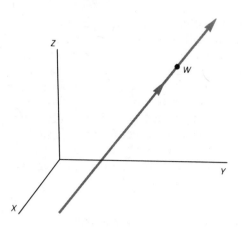

kind *a priori* and were, therefore, innate?

With the help of Lorentz's formulae it is possible to calculate the speed of light in a moving medium whose refractive index is n. One finds, not surprisingly, the same result as that of Fizeau. Another consequence of Lorentz's 'transformation rules' is that all measurements of the size of objects moving relative to the observer are shortened in the direction of motion precisely in the way already assumed by Lorentz and Fitzgerald (section 40). This latter effect does not destroy the explanation we gave for the result of Michelson and Morley's experiment, bearing in mind the constancy of the velocity of light. It follows, among other things, from the theory that a moving observer sees the frequency of light oscillations change in the leg of the interferometer parallel to the direction of motion. The two effects compensate each other exactly.

Another phenomenon from the optics of moving media must be mentioned here. We said above that the frequency of the oscillations for an observer in motion relative to the oscillating source is changed; this phenomenon is called the *Doppler effect* and is, therefore, in fact a relativistic phenomenon. It can be observed in the pitch of the sound emitted by a passing hooting car, and also in the light emitted by stars very far removed from earth. If a star is moving away from the earth the frequency of the light received here falls. The spectral lines emitted by the stars (see section 48) are shifted to the red side of the spectrum. This 'red shift' is observed in all directions for those stars far removed from earth; one can describe this as an expansion of our universe.

45 The kinds of electromagnetic radiation

Let us consider for a moment longer the objects we call electromagnetic waves. We have already met the Hertz waves and have now recognised light as being of them also. We have already mentioned earlier in this book that next to visible light there is also 'infra-red' and 'ultra-violet' radiation. These kinds of radiation are part of the spectrum of 'black body radiation' which we discussed in section 35 and which we shall mention again in section 49. In general one can say that bodies at a rather low temperature (for example a stove) send out more radiation in the infra-red, of which the wavelength is larger than 780 nm. As the temperature rises (to that, for example of an electric bulb) a large amount of the radiation appears in the visible region between 780 and 380 nm. At higher temperatures still (such as those in the sun) much ultra-violet radiation is produced with wavelengths smaller than 380 nm. The infra-red and ultra-violet radiation behave exactly like visible light; working with them is made more difficult because materials which are transparent to visible light are often opaque to that part of the spectrum lying just outside the visible region. In the far ultra-violet (λ smaller than 100 nm) air begins to absorb strongly, so that experiments dealing with such radiation must be performed in a vacuum.

For even smaller wavelengths one comes into the region of x-ray radiation (λ smaller than 1 nm). They are also to be considered as electro-magnetic waves and they show all the properties of these. On the scale of x-ray wavelengths matter appears quite different from when the wavelength of light is used as a measure. The distances between atoms are small relative to the wavelength of visible light, namely of the order of a few tenths of one nm. But they are just of the same order of magnitude as the wavelengths in the x-ray region. For visible light matter, therefore, seems to be a continuum such as water and air, which for us have no substructure. For x-rays it is somewhat different: the separate atoms in matter can be distinguished with very small wavelengths. A row of atoms is for x-ray radiation what a grating is for visible light. In each case the same phenomena show up: when the radiation falls on the grating light is directed in certain directions which depend on the wavelength of the radiation and the distance between the elements of the grating. When a beam of x-rays of a given wavelength falls on a crystal the radiation is directed in certain directions which depend on the distances between the atoms (see figure 128). Now a crystal is a three dimensional construction of atoms; because of this the situation is somewhat more complicated than for an ordinary grating, which is a one dimensional array of sources. Yet the structure of a crystal has in many cases been successfully obtained from the complicated patterns which are formed by the diffraction of x-rays in crystals. X-ray diffraction is,

Figure 128. The crystal as a grating for x-rays.
The diffraction pattern, caused by light coming
in from the left, is shown on the screen.

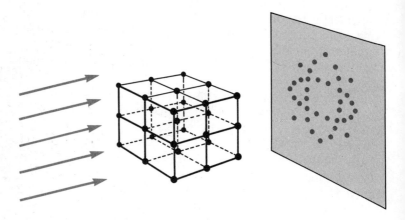

therefore, an important tool in the study of the structure of matter.

We leave now the region of small wavelength to nose around a little in the spectrum of wavelengths larger than one thousand nm. A length of one thousand nm is one millionth of a metre, and is, therefore, also called one micron (μ). One ascribes the wavelengths of one to about one hundred microns to the infra-red region: the absorption spectrum (see section 47) of many materials transparent to visible light consists in this region of 'bands' of many close-lying wavelengths. Water is a good example of a material showing such absorption; because of the strong absorption the transmission of infra-red radiation through an atmosphere containing water vapour (and also through the so-called 'water-like fluid' of the eye) is impossible. From one hundred micron, which is equal to one tenth of a millimetre, begin the micro-waves; these are

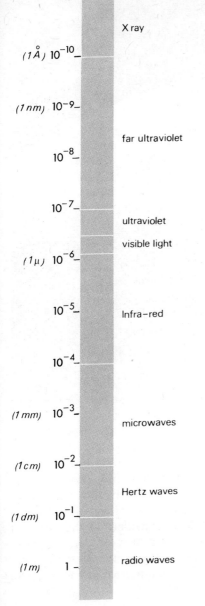

203

Figure 129. Regions of the electromagnetic spectrum.

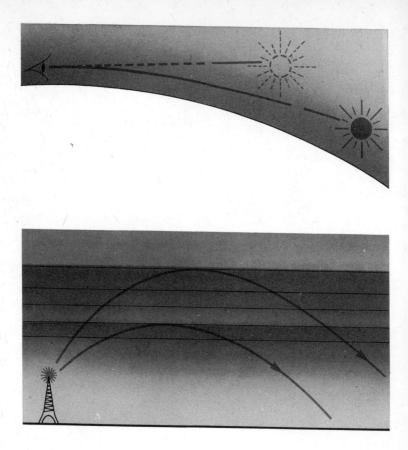

really neither one thing nor the other: they combine the properties of Hertz waves (with wavelengths of the order of centimetres) and infra-red light. They are difficult to create and to handle and are much used in the investigation of molecular structure, which can be understood considering what we said above about the absorption spectrum of molecules. Following the micro-waves we get the Hertz waves (see section 43) and at even longer wavelengths, decimetres and longer, we finally get radio waves.

Figures 130 and 131. *Top* The apparent
altitude of the sun. *Bottom* Total
reflection in the ionosphere.

205

We have now handled in rough outline the whole electro-magnetic spectrum. The whole story is summarised in figure 129. We now want to draw an analogy with the behaviour of radio waves with one example. In the atmosphere the density of the air becomes steadily smaller as we go up; the refractive index also follows this relationship. From this it follows that we *see* the sun go down later than we would have done if there had been no atmosphere: in figure 130 one can see how a ray of light coming from the low standing sun reaches the observer via a curved path; we therefore see the sun higher up in the sky because of the presence of an atmosphere with a refractive index which is not the same everywhere. Something similar occurs with radio waves. In the ionosphere, at great heights (up to 400 km), there are layers with rather large refractive index for radio waves. In such a layer the refractive index changes with the height and because of this it can occur, as is sketched in figure 131, that a beam of radio waves emitted by a station is totally reflected by one of these layers. Where this beam reaches the earth again one has good reception of this particular station. We have said enough about the electromagnetic field; we shall now see what the relation is with the structure of matter.

8 Oscillators and photons

46 The oscillator model

In section 43 we described the experiments of Heinrich Hertz which he performed using dipole antennas as radiation source and receiver. We now describe more precisely the field emitted by a dipole (see figure 132). The wavefronts, at a distance from the dipole p, large compared to the wavelength (and therefore also to the size of the dipole which is approximately half a wavelength long for resonance; see section 43), have the form of spherical surfaces. The E vector points along a great circle, the H vector along a meridian. We see that here transverse waves are produced: the direction of propagation S lies along the normal to the spherical surface and is, therefore, perpendicular to E and H. The intensity of the emitted radiation is not the same in all directions; it is zero in the direction of the length of the dipole, and reaches a maximum in a direction perpendicular to this.

   We would not describe the field of a dipole in such detail were it not so important for what will follow later. Following an idea of Lorentz, one can explain a good deal of the optical properties of materials by supposing that they are made up of dipole-like elements: the oscillators. In the nineteenth century it had been discovered that an important particle present in all matter is the electron, which is a small, extremely light particle with a known fixed negative charge. Matter as a whole is generally electrically neutral and there must, therefore, also be positive charges. In metals, the electrons, or at any rate some of them, are free to move in the fixed structure of positive nuclei. The optical behaviour of metals is particularly noteworthy for its strong absorption; we shall, therefore, discuss only the non-conductors such as glass, for they are more interesting for the optician. In non-

Figure 132. The field of a dipole.   207

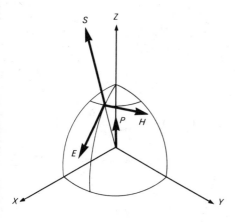

conductors the electrons are bound to the nuclei and one can, in the first approximation, suppose the binding to be elastic (such as in a spring: the harder one pulls it out the larger is the force needed to do this). An elastically bound electron we call an electron oscillator.* We consider now one such electron oscillator (see figure 133) which we depict as a negative charge at one end of a spring, the other end of which is attached to the positive lattice of the material. If the negative charge gets a push, an 'impulse', it goes into oscillation about an equilibrium distance. But a moving charge is a current; a current which goes backwards and forwards is called an alternating current. We see, therefore, that these oscillators look remarkably like the dipoles of Hertz (section 43) and also strongly resemble the current elements for which we

* One can also imagine other oscillators: in a molecule there are atoms which are mutually elastically bound and which can oscillate, as can also the ions in a crystal of household salt (Na⁺ Cl⁻).

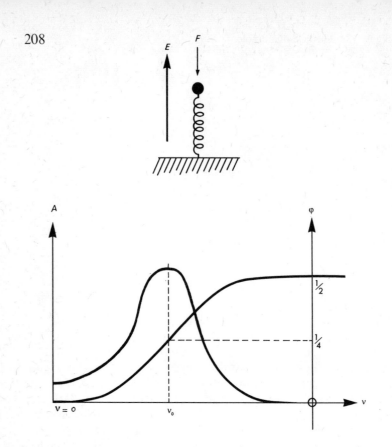

calculated the field in section 41. When an electromagnetic wave, for example a light wave, reaches an oscillator, the oscillator reacts particularly to the E vector of the wave, just as did the dipoles of Hertz.

Because an electron oscillator has a negative charge, the force F which the field exerts on it is pointed in the direction opposite to the momentary value of the E vector at the place (see figure 133). The E vector of a light wave oscillates very rapidly (it must be remembered that the frequency of light is of the order of $5 . 10^{14}$ Hertz). Under the influence of the light

Figures 133, 134 and 135. *Top left* The electron
oscillator. *Bottom left* Amplitude and phase of the
oscillator as a function of the frequency.
Below An incoming wave is eliminated by a
large number of oscillators and re-emitted.

209

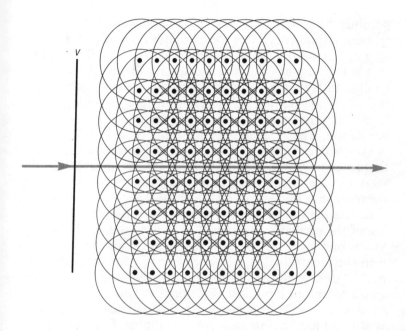

wave the oscillator will vibrate at the same frequency. We are
interested in the amplitude and the phase of these vibrations.
The amplitude of the oscillator is a maximum at a particular
frequency, the resonance frequency, which depends on the
mass of the electron and the stiffness of the elastic binding or
spring; we met this resonance phenomenon already with the
dipoles of Hertz. With regard to the phase of the oscillations,
the following is to be noted. In a very slowly varying field the
oscillator will be able to keep pace with the variation. The
phase difference will be zero. When the frequency of the field

becomes high, that is to say considerably higher than the resonance frequency, then the oscillator falls behind in phase by a half an oscillation. It is then in anti-phase with the field, that is to say, when the field has a crest the oscillator is in a trough. In the region around the resonance frequency where the amplitude reaches its largest value the phase lag of the oscillator with respect to the field is about one quarter of an oscillation. The behaviour of the amplitude A and phase φ is sketched in figure 134, where ν_0 indicates the resonance frequency. The mass and stiffness are responsible for the inertia of the oscillator: it in turn determines the position of the resonance frequency and the phase lag.

In relation to this we must also pay attention to the damping of the oscillator, by which we understand the following. When one gives an oscillator an impulse and leaves it undisturbed thereafter, it will, after having gone through many oscillations, finally return to rest at its equilibrium distance. In the meantime it has lost all its energy. This happens in part because an oscillator emits energy in the form of radiation: it is after all identical to an oscillating dipole. For a small part the energy is lost because the binding mechanism shows internal friction. The damping is responsible for the fact that the oscillator does not use up all its energy in oscillating with ever increasing amplitude when it is in an alternating field of just the right frequency, that is to say the resonance frequency. To make concrete the continuous growth of the amplitude upon driving at the resonance frequency, one can think of a swing which at each right moment is given a push, whereby it goes all the higher; but here too the damping limits the amplitude. Figure 134 shows a damped oscillator. A result of the damping is also that the resonance peak of the amplitude becomes lower and broader.

What happens now when a plane light wave falls on a sheet of matter? We have drawn the situation in figure 135; for ease of description we assume the infalling wave to be parallel to the interface; the material is represented by several rows of oscillators, the distance between them being small compared to the wavelength of the light (this is right for light but for x-rays matter looks quite different, see section 45). The oscillators will vibrate with the light; this costs the light wave much of its energy, because there are so many oscillators. The infalling wave, therefore, disappears rapidly: after a couple of wavelengths it is no more than a ghost of its former self, moving through the material with the speed c and the wavelength λ of the infalling wave.

The oscillators now take over the work. The secondary emission which they send out is transmitted from row to row until the last row sends it out again into the vacuum. The oscillators also emit light towards the left: this forms the radiation reflected at the interface, as we would normally describe it. From the behaviour of the individual oscillators, such as we described above, it becomes understandable that the secondary wave has a smaller speed and wavelength than the infalling wave. The oscillators emit their radiation principally in directions making only a small angle with the surface perpendicular to the direction of oscillation (see the description of the dipole field at the beginning of this paragraph). In this plane the oscillator radiates in all directions. The waves of the different oscillators interfere with each other. If we consider the row of oscillators as a row of radiation sources with equal phase, then from symmetry considerations we see that the overall secondary wave will be parallel to this row (see figure 136); in short, the light emitted to the left by the oscillators forms a plane wavefront together with

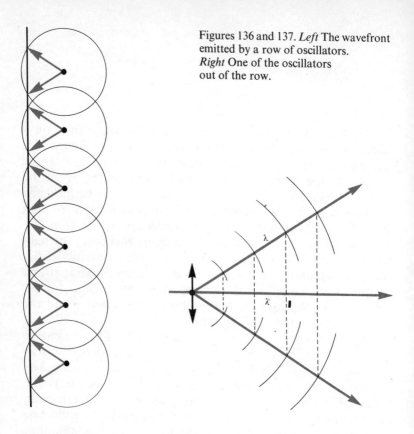

Figures 136 and 137. *Left* The wavefront emitted by a row of oscillators. *Right* One of the oscillators out of the row.

the waves which are emitted to the right. But these waves, seen in the direction of the total secondary wave, have a speed and a wavelength which is smaller than that seen when looked at in the direction of their own motion. In figure 137 we see that the wavelength in the direction of the secondary wave, λ', is obtained by projecting the original wavelength λ upon this direction; the same applies to the speed.

Another mechanism to do with the transmission emerges from this projection effect: in the neighbourhood of the resonance frequency and above it, the oscillators, as we saw, fall behind in phase relative to the incoming wave. The radia-

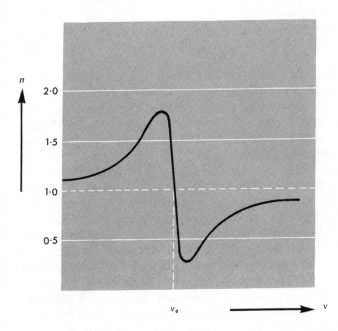

Figure 138. The behaviour of the refractive index in the neighbourhood of an absorption line that we imagine to be in the ultra-violet. The visible region of the spectrum lies to the left of v_0.

tion energy is, as it were, held back a little. For this reason also, the speed of propagation V is reduced and, therefore, also the wavelength, since the frequency v remains constant (and $V = v\lambda$). We see that this oscillator model describes the behaviour of the material in interaction with light in a most elegant manner. As we shall very soon see, however, there are difficulties which arise when there are several resonance frequencies associated with the same atom (see next section). In figure 138 we have indicated the behaviour of the refractive index $n = \dfrac{c}{V}$ in the neighbourhood of a resonance frequency in the ultra-violet. The left-hand part of this graph agrees closely with the behaviour of the refractive index in most glasses.

We conclude from this that the atoms of which glass is made (the atoms of silicone are for the most part responsible) have their resonance in the ultra-violet. The dispersion – that is, the change of the refractive index with the wavelength – becomes larger towards the blue; in the ultra-violet region the glass begins to absorb strongly. This becomes understandable when we know that the energy dissipated through the damping process is more or less proportional to the amplitude of the oscillators; in the neighbourhood of the resonance both amplitude and damping are at a maximum. That most kinds of glass also absorb strongly in the infra-red one nowadays ascribes to the presence of water in the glass, absorbed during the process of manufacture, in particular during the cooling after the glass has come out of the ovens. The water molecules form molecular oscillators because the atoms are mutually bound by elastic forces; since atoms are much heavier than electrons these oscillators are slower, so that their resonances lie at lower frequencies, in the infra-red.

47 Selective absorption

Making use of what we learned in the previous section about the oscillator model, we shall now describe the phenomenon of *selective absorption*. By selective absorption we understand the following. Suppose that by heating we have produced some sodium vapour in a closed space (see figure 139) and we now direct a beam of white light through the vapour. After passage through the space the spectrum of the white light is produced with a grating or a prism (in the

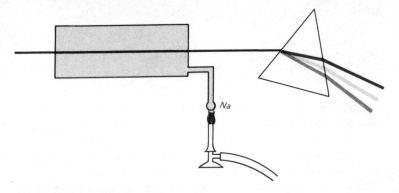

figure a prism is shown). Dark lines can be seen in the spectrum; with sodium vapour there are in particular two lines lying close to each other in the yellow (a so-called doublet, at 589 and 589·5 nm). The sodium vapour absorbs strongly at particular wavelengths, hence the name selective absorption. We remark incidentally that such dark lines also appear in the spectrum of sunlight. They were discovered first by Fraunhofer with the help of his grating spectrograph and were ascribed to selective absorption of the sun's radiation in the outer layers of its atmosphere. The most intense of these 'Fraunhofer lines' are also obtainable on earth by replacing the sodium vapour by water vapour in the experiment illustrated in figure 139. One deduces from this that the atmosphere of the sun contains much water vapour.

The explanation of the phenomenon of selective absorption lies in the fact that the resonance frequency of the oscillators belonging to the sodium atoms lies in the yellow. The sodium atoms react only to radiation which lies in the neighbourhood of their resonance frequency; they absorb such radiation and re-emit part of it in all directions; the light which goes into the prism contains, therefore, considerably less of the yellow colour than does the incoming white light. We draw attention to the fact that the optical properties of sodium *vapour* are quite different from that of solid sodium. The latter is a metal, which is to say that the atoms release electrons which are then free to go where they will; the remainder of the atoms which, because of the missing electrons, are positively charged and are, therefore, ions, form a lattice through which the electronic 'fluid' flows. In sodium vapour the atoms are only very slightly subject to interactions amongst themselves, and they therefore keep each their own electrons.

One can study the transition from the gaseous form to the metallic form of sodium by continually increasing the vapour pressure in the absorption cell shown in figure 139. The first thing that one sees happening is that the absorption lines become broader. This occurs because the atoms begin to interfere with each other through collision and, as it were, make the determination of the frequency at which they absorb less accurate. One needs an infinitely long time to determine a frequency exactly; we said in section 5 that a precisely defined harmonic wave consists of an infinitely long chain of crests and waves; it lasts an eternity before it has passed the observer. Thus the shorter the time allowed for measurement, the less accurate the determination of the frequency. The analogy is valid for atoms: the shorter the time that they remain undisturbed the less opportunity they have of determining the frequency at which radiation is absorbed or emitted. The 'life-time' for atoms becomes limited by the increase in the number of collision; and so the absorption line is broadened. At even higher pressures one begins to see absorption over the whole spectrum and also strong reflection of the incoming light at the surface formed by the outer edge of the vapour. In other words the vapour begins to behave more and more like a metal. As the atoms are brought closer together two things generally happen: the broadening of the number of frequencies to which they respond and the beginning of the ordering of the atoms so that the separate atoms begin to work together and pheno-

Figure 140. Selective emission.   217

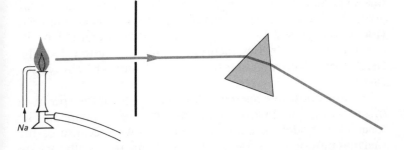

mena such as the above-mentioned reflection begin to occur. The oscillator model teaches us that there is a connection between these two tendencies. If one may consider the separate atoms as oscillators then one must consider a piece of solid material to be made up of *coupled* oscillators. A study of mechanics shows us that a system composed of N coupled oscillators each with three directions of motion will in general have $3N$ resonance frequencies. One must look upon solid matter as an ordered array of coupled oscillators: a gas (or vapour) consists of uncoupled or unordered atoms; one must, therefore, make a sharp distinction between the optical properties of these two forms of matter.

48 Selective emission

The opposite of selective absorption is selective emission of radiation. If in the flame of, for example, a Bunsen burner (see figure 140), one sows certain sodium salts then the flame emits a bright yellow light; using a grating or a prism one can check that the light is again the same doublet (589–589·5 nm) that we dealt with in the previous section. One can perform this experiment just as well with other metals; each metal gives its characteristic spectrum. In this way each material can be recognised by the spectrum which is emitted by its oscillators; we already mentioned this in section 13. The spectra of selective absorption and emission are always the same.

We must now ask ourselves how the shape of the spectrum of, for example hydrogen atoms, can be explained. The 'oscillator model' of emission is as follows: because of the thermal motion of the material in the flame the oscillators are knocked about and they, therefore, begin to oscillate and emit radiation. We took the hydrogen atom as an example because this atom has a particularly simple structure: it consists of one electron which is coupled to a positive nucleus. The oscillator model makes us expect in this case a simple structure for the spectrum: one resonance frequency, or at most three, for the three directions of space. This expectation is completely knocked to the ground by the experiment: the spectrum of the hydrogen atom consists of far more than three lines (see figure 141). To rescue the oscillator theory one might suppose that the emitted signal consists of the main tone and overtones just as it does with a clock. But upon investigation even this supposition is shown to be unfounded. It would lead us to expect in the spectrum lines with the frequencies v (the fundamental tone), $2v$, $3v$, and so on; thus wavelengths of $\lambda = \dfrac{c}{v}$; $\frac{1}{2}\lambda$; $\frac{1}{3}\lambda$ and so forth. The strongest line in the hydrogen atom spectrum is the so-called red H line at 656 nm (shown in figure 23, section 13). We would, therefore, expect a line at 328 nm (the first overtone) in the ultra-violet. There is no such line. There are many other lines in the hydrogen atom spectrum whose ordering escapes us at first sight.

The Englishman Lyman (1914), a man brought up in the classical tradition, noted the similarity between the visible lines of the hydrogen atom spectrum and a row of pillars seen in perspective. Balmer (1885) gave for the first time a formula for the frequencies of the visible lines of the hydrogen atom spectrum. His equation reads:—

$$v(2,m) = R \left(\frac{1}{2^2} - \frac{1}{m^2} \right)$$

Here R is a constant and m is a whole number larger than two. We call $v(2,m)$ the mth line of the second Balmer series. We see that this series of lines goes to a limit as m increases, the limit being $v(2,\infty) = \frac{R}{4}$. The lines come to lie very close to each other (the difference between $\frac{1}{m}$ and $\frac{1}{m+1}$ is small for large values of m), in the neighbourhood of the series limit. The smallest frequency of this series is $v(2,3) = R \left(\frac{1}{2^2} - \frac{1}{3^2} \right) = \frac{5R}{36}$. This corresponds to the H line, at 656 nm, so that we can calculate R. One can describe the frequencies of the lines of the hydrogen atom's spectrum with the general formula

$$v(n,m) = R \left(\frac{1}{n^2} - \frac{1}{m^2} \right).$$

Indeed it comes out that the spectrum of the hydrogen atom fits this formula exactly. The series with n equal to one was discovered by Lyman and it lies in the ultra-violet and begins at $v(1,2) = \frac{3}{4}R$. the wavelength corresponding to this is $\lambda(1,2) = 121 \cdot 5$ nm. According to this formula the largest

220

Figure 141. The spectrum of the hydrogen atom.

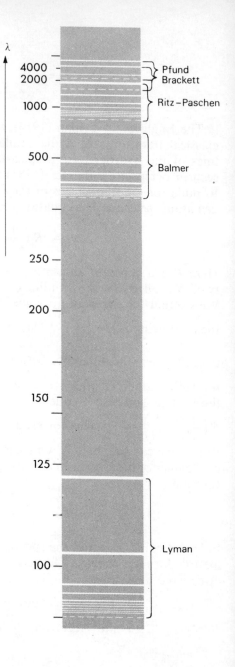

frequency which can be emitted by hydrogen atoms is $v(1,\infty) = R$. This frequency corresponds to the wavelength (in a vacuum) $\lambda(1,\infty) = 90.5$ nm in the ultra-violet. The idea of a 'largest frequency' does not fit the oscillator model. According to mechanics, there can be overtones of steadily increasing frequency. On a violin one can always obtain higher overtones, in principle up to infinity. But there is more: upon careful measurement it is seen that the line $\lambda(1,\infty) = 90.5$ nm abuts on a spectrum of smaller wavelengths (that is to say higher frequencies) and this spectrum is *continuous*. That really is the limit; a continuous spectrum from an atom! All in all we can now see that the oscillator model does not give a satisfactory explanation for the shape and structure of the atomic spectra.

The failure of the oscillator model has eventually led to an even more comprehensive and fundamental revision of the elementary physical concepts than did the difficulties associated with the theory of the aether. In the following pages we discuss two fields of physics from which these new concepts originated, namely black-body radiation (section 49) and the photo-electric effect (section 50). Thereafter we return again to the spectra and the structure of atoms (section 51).

49 Black-body radiation

We have already mentioned a few properties of black-body radiation in section 35. We learned there that one understands by 'black-body radiation' an electromagnetic field in a space which is surrounded on all sides by matter and in which there are no light sources. The spectrum of black-body radiation is determined solely by the temperature of the surrounding material; we showed the shape of this spectrum for several different temperatures in figure 105. From the theory of heat or thermodynamics one can deduce that the energy of the radiation field is proportional to the fourth power of the temperature. We shall now show how the spectral energy distribution (energy as a function of wavelength) can be determined at a particular temperature. For this we must first determine whether all wavelengths really are present in the field. We now take what, at first sight, seems to be a very risky step: we assume that the walls of the space in which the black-body radiation is present reflect this radiation to a large degree. This seems to be an unjustified assumption since in general it is not true for walls of a cavity in a solid. It is, however, less stupid than one might think: it is the temperature of the walls that determines the energy spectrum, so that the nature of the wall is not important for this (only the exchange of energy with the material becomes more difficult when the reflection is increased, wherefore a disturbance of the equilibrium between radiation and the material takes longer to settle). The cavity with reflecting walls between which a light wave is reflected backwards and forwards, we call a *resonant cavity*; we have already met one such cavity when we discussed the Fabry-Perot interferometer (see section 25). In the case of the Fabry-Perot interferometer we saw that only certain frequencies could remain after some time in the field of a resonant cavity, the wavelengths corresponding to these frequencies depending on the dimensions of the cavity. In the Fabry-Perot interferometer a frequency was allowed when a whole number of half wavelengths corresponded to the length of the interferometer. The result of this was that the number of allowed frequencies, or *modes* (ways of oscillating) was proportional to the length of the instrument. The same applies for all resonant cavities: only certain frequencies, the modes, can occur in the field, and the number of them in any small region of the spectrum is proportional to the volume of the cavity.

One can compare the modes in a cavity with the swell of organ music in a great cathedral: the noise is made up of the large number of different tones. In order to know the total intensity one must know the strength, or intensity, of each tone as well as how many pipes there are in each register of the organ. When one calculates the number of modes in a cavity it turns out that the spectral density (the number of modes in a small region of the spectrum between wavelengths λ and $\lambda + \Delta\lambda$, where $\Delta\lambda$ is very small compared to λ) is inversely proportional to the fourth power of λ. That is the number of 'organ pipes per register'.

The calculation of the energy of each mode is a separate problem. Classical statistical mechanics (the science which deals with systems made up of many components) led to the conclusion that, whenever one considered the modes as separate components of the system, which can exchange their energy via oscillators in the wall (the oscillator model peeps round the corner again here), then the average energy of such a component is equal to kT where k is a constant called Boltzmann's constant and T is the temperature. In this system all modes have the same energy. But now a difficulty arises: the number of modes is, as we saw, proportional to $\frac{1}{\lambda^4}$. This means that there is an infinitely large amount of energy in the field, because the number of modes becomes infinite as the wavelength becomes smaller and, as we said, each mode has the same energy, namely kT. Furthermore the energy spectrum predicted by this calculation is quite different from

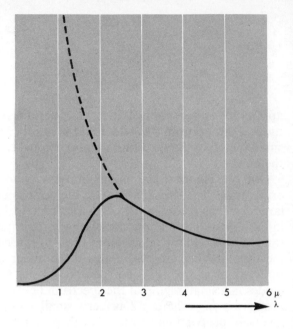

that experimentally found in section 35. In figure 142 we have shown the spectrum calculated for a temperature of 1000°K together with the experimental spectrum determined at this temperature. We see that the agreement is very good at long wavelengths.

In order to escape from these difficulties Max Planck (1858–1947) put forward a hypothesis which was as simple as it was unheard of: he said that the modes could only have an amount of energy which was an integral multiple of the smallest energy or *energy quantum* of size $h\nu$ (ν is the frequency of the mode, and h is a constant which was later called Planck's constant). According to classical physics this is quite nonsensical: the system can in any circumstance have an energy which is distributed continuously over all possible values. Planck's hypothesis has become one of the corner-

Figure 142. The spectral energy distribution
of black body radiation at a
temperature of 1,000°K (727°C). The full
line according to Planck; the dotted
line according to the classical theory.

225

stones of modern science. The result for the theory of black-body radiation was that Planck could now calculate an energy distribution over the modes which did not contain the above-mentioned disagreeable properties of the classical distribution: according to Planck the modes with small wavelength have on average such a small amount of energy, that the total energy remains finite even though the number of modes rises without limit. The energy spectrum calculated in this way agrees very accurately with the observations. In the following section we shall see how very fruitful this *quantum hypothesis* has been in modern physics. We point out now already that one can consider quite naturally the energy packets hv as 'light particles', whereby we have returned again to Newton's old theory (compare with section 3).

50 The photo-electric effect

Support for the quantum hypothesis came from the photo-electric effect. When a metal surface is irradiated with light one can observe that electrons are ejected from the metal. If at the same time one creates an electric field (see figure 143) between the metal surface and another piece of metal further away, which is brought to a positive potential, one can then suck away the electrons towards the positive electrode. In the conductor connecting the two pieces of metal a current is now produced whose intensity is proportional to the number of electrons ejected per unit time from the metal surface. It is a fact that the number of electrons emitted diminishes proportionately as the wavelength of the light increases; at a particular wavelength the production of electrons stops altogether, however much the amount of irradiating light may be. With the help of the oscillator model one cannot explain

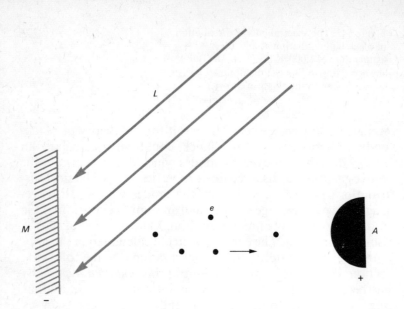

this phenomenon. According to this model one argues as if the electrons were apples on a tree, which must fall if the tree is shaken sufficiently hard; with what frequency one shakes should not be important. But one cannot thereby throw any light upon the fact that there is one longest wavelength above which emission of electrons is impossible.

The quantum hypothesis does get us out of our difficulties here also. This was shown by Albert Einstein (1879–1955). The smallest amount of energy which a mode can give off or absorb, we saw above to be a quantum of magnitude hv. One can, therefore, consider the incoming light as a large number of light particles or *photons*. Each of these photons has the chance of being slowed up by an electron. The electron then feels stronger and can perhaps leave the metal; the chances become larger as the energy of the photon increases. The energy of a photon is hv, proportional, therefore, to the frequency; when the energy falls below a particular value then it is no longer enough to free the electron.

Figure 143. The photo-electric effect.
227

Negative electrons are ejected from the metal
surface M by the oncoming light beam L.
The electrons move towards the anode A,
which has a positive potential relative to M.

To return to our analogy with the tree and the apples: the quantum theory sees it like this. One throws all sorts of stones at the apples; all stones have the same speed; the lighter a stone is the smaller its chance to knock an apple from the tree, stones which are too small have simply no chance at all. Thus: one cannot cause the emission of electrons from the metal surface with a radiation whose photons are too small, that is to say with too small a frequency, or too *large* a wavelength. By measuring the energy of the emitted electrons Einstein could determine the value of Planck's constant; this value agreed exactly with that determined from the energy distribution of black-body radiation.

51 Spectra and atoms

We now resume our study of the spectra emitted by the atoms, which we abandoned in section 48. We still stick to the example of the hydrogen atom's spectrum; we remember that the frequency of the spectral lines of hydrogen could be written as the difference between two terms R/n^2 and R/m^2 where n and m are whole numbers, with m larger than n. The quantum theory, which first came to the fore in the previous sections, taught us that the energy of a radiation field could only increase or decrease its value by an amount equal to one quantum $h\nu$ each time. Where do these quanta, also called photons, come from? In all probability, they come from atoms which emit the radiation. From this it follows, or so argued Bohr, that atoms also must have the property that they can only absorb or emit certain determined quantities of light energy. When a photon is emitted, the energy of an atom, which was first E_n, is reduced by an amount $h\nu$. The remaining energy of the atom we call E_m. In the whole of physics the law of the conservation of energy holds: the energy of an isolated system remains constant. If we now consider the system 'atom-radiation field' we can write

$$hv = E_n - E_m$$

We show this relation diagrammatically in figure 144. E_n and E_m are two 'energy levels' of the atom; whenever the atom goes from the upper to the lower level it emits an amount of energy hv in the form of a photon; the distance between energy levels determines the size of the frequency of the emitted light according to the above formula. According to Balmer's formula we could write the emitted frequency as

$$hv = \frac{hR}{n^2} - \frac{hR}{m^2}$$

(in this equation we have multiplied both sides of Balmer's formula by h). By comparing the two formulae we see that the simplest answer would be that the energy levels of the hydrogen atom are given by

$$E_k = \frac{hR}{k^2}$$

(k is a whole number).

Since the hydrogen atom never emits spectral *lines* other than those which can be calculated by Balmer's formula, we are led to the conclusion that these are the only possible energy levels of the hydrogen atom. How then must we explain the existence of energy levels in the hydrogen atom? The solution of this problem is, so we saw, closely related to the explanation of the genesis of the photons; therefore, we devote the rest of this section to this question.

Figures 144 and 145. *Left* Energy levels and
Bohr's equation $E_n - E_m = h\nu$.
Right The hydrogen atom according to Bohr.

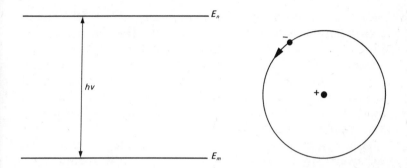

Through the researches of Rutherford, Thomson, Bohr
and many others, it became apparent that atoms consist of a
positive nucleus around which a number of (negative) electrons move like planets round the sun. The hydrogen atom
has only one electron (see figure 145), and is, therefore, the
simplest of all atoms. One can calculate the energy of an atom
whose nucleus (about 2,000 times as heavy as one electron)
is at rest, by equating the energy possessed by an electron
moving in a particular orbit to the electrostatic energy caused
by the attraction between nucleus and electron. The energy is
given by an expression in which the radius of the orbit
appears as a variable and the mass and charge of the electron
and nucleus as constants. From this, however, it is not clear
why an electron can only have certain energy levels, that is to
say can only travel in certain orbits. Classical physics is of
little use here. According to it the periodically moving
electron (analogous to an alternating current) must emit
radiation. If an electron starts moving in a given orbit, with a
given energy, then this energy must gradually be reduced and,
therefore, the radius of the orbit becomes smaller. The atom

would thus run through a scale of energy values, which is in contradiction with our picture of discrete energy levels. Finally, according to the classical model the electron would, because of the emission of radiation with ever smaller wavelength, finally crash into the nucleus: the notorious 'ultraviolet catastrophe'. An atom such as we have drawn in figure 145 cannot, therefore, according to classical mechanics, even remain in existence!

A new approach to the problem was needed. And this was discovered by Louis de Broglie (born 1892) who enunciated the following hypothesis: just as light waves have a corpuscular character, so have material particles such as electrons a certain 'wave aspect'. The wavelength of these waves is (by hypothesis) given by the equation

$$\lambda = \frac{h}{p}$$

where p is the product of the mass and the velocity, called momentum of the material particle. What then is the connection between these matter-waves and the radius of the orbit of an electron in a hydrogen atom? In order to see this we return once again to the Fabry-Perot interferometer. In figure 146a we see such an instrument; we remember its most remarkable property; the mode of the radiation field between the mirrors S can only remain in existence if the length of the interferometer equals a whole number of half wavelengths. So it is also with the wavelength of an 'electron wave' in an atom: the circumference of the orbit of an electron must equal a whole number of wavelengths of the electron wave. So only certain orbits are possible, and thus only certain energy levels. In figure 146b we have drawn a few allowed orbits, together with the nodes K and antinodes B of the

Figures 146a and 146b. *Top* The Fabry-Perot interferometer. *Bottom* Allowed orbits and electron waves.

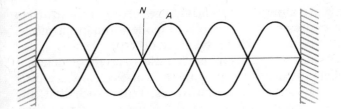

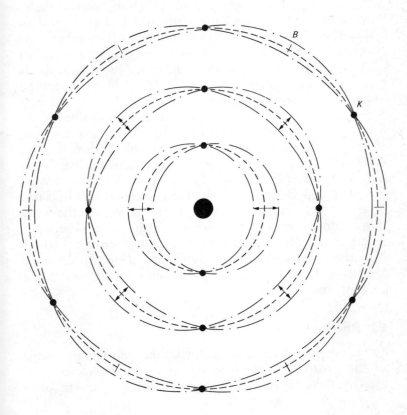

electron wave along such an orbit. The theory of these orbits was first expressed in terms of the modern quantum mechanics by Schrödinger, Heisenberg and others.

We now want to philosophise a little over these material waves. One must not imagine these as if electrons are little ships on an ocean of electron waves; rather such that, the larger the intensity of the material wave is at a particular place, the more chance one has of seeing an electron there. We cannot therefore ever know more about an electron than that it is more likely to be here than there. Let us look at the electrons in an atom. The electron wave cannot be restricted to just the orbit which we showed in figure 146b; this is just as with light rays, where an infinitely 'thin' ray also proved impossible because of diffraction. The electron wave is 'smeared out' over the whole atom, and on both sides of the orbit there is a chance that one might meet the electron, although the greatest chance is that one should meet it in the *neighbourhood* of the Bohr orbit. Can electron waves show diffraction phenomena just as water and light waves? Davisson and Gerner discovered that the exposure of a thin layer of metal to an electron beam produced the same diffraction patterns as are obtained with x-rays. The wavelength of the electrons becomes shorter as their speed (therefore, their momentum $p = mV$) increases. One reaches wavelengths of the order of $0 \cdot 1$ nm, thus approximately as large as x-ray waves.

52 Photons

In the previous section we dealt with the quantum mechanics of the hydrogen atom, whereby the wave character of an electron was the central property. The wavelength of an

Figure 147. The light pressure, twice as large on reflection as on absorption.

233

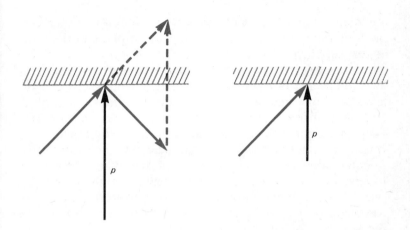

electron wave was, as we saw, given by the quotient of h, Planck's constant, and the momentum p. Going over to the quantum theory of light, we ask ourselves the question: can one also ascribe a momentum to photons given by the equation $p = \dfrac{h}{\lambda}$? This is indeed the case. In section 43 we saw that Lebedew measured the pressure of light. Well now, just as the momentum of gas molecules is responsible for gas pressure, so is the momentum of the light particles responsible for the light pressure. Upon reflection at a surface the photon changes the direction of its velocity; the light pressure on a reflecting surface is twice as large as at an absorbing surface where the momentum does not change sign but becomes zero. In figure 147 we have sketched both cases. The quantum theory of light thus gives us an unforced and clear explanation for the phenomenon of light pressure.

We venture now to give to the light waves the same meaning as we ascribed to material waves in the previous section:

the intensity of the wave at a particular point is a measure of the probability that a photon exists at that place, at the time of measurement. In the light of this we now look at the interference experiment of Young (see figure 148). The question which intrigues us is: if one performs this experiment with one photon, through which slit does the photon go? The answer must be: one cannot say, because the question is not properly formulated. In order to determine where the photon arrives on the screen S one must first calculate the field with the help of the wave theory (of Maxwell or, if one wishes, of Huygens). Now the field from one slit is essentially different from that from two slits. It is not true that the field of two slits gives an intensity which is the sum of the intensity from each slit taken separately. Interference occurs (at least when the slits are illuminated with coherent light); in other words, both slits determine whereabouts on S one has a good chance of finding a photon (a maximum of the interference pattern) and where this is most unlikely (in the dark interference line).

When both slits are illuminated with incoherent light, one can determine through which slit a given photon has come, at least in special circumstances. In figure 149 we draw the intensity on the screen S; in this case it is the sum of the diffraction patterns from the separate slits. Suppose now that one maximum of the diffraction pattern of the slit O_1, covers up exactly a minimum of the slit O_2 at a point p. Then for a photon observed at p one can with great certainty say that it came through O_1. We draw attention to the fact that this experiment could not be performed with one photon. For coherent light comes from a single source, and, therefore, if one wishes to illuminate O_1 and O_2 with incoherent light, one must use two sources. In a field of two sources there must be

Figures 148 and 149. *Top* Young's
experiment in coherent light.
Bottom The same in incoherent light.

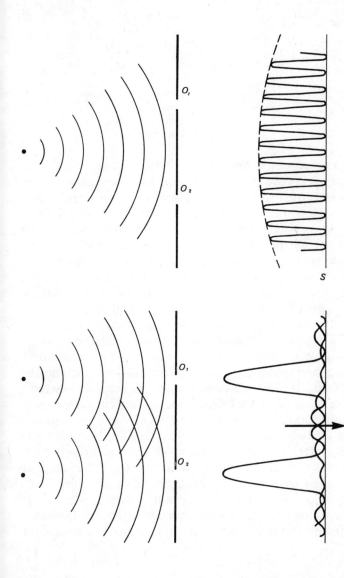

236

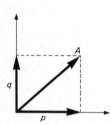

Figure 150. The state of polarisation of the photon A, made up of the components p and q; p is stopped by the Nicol, q is transmitted.

at least two photons. And this proves our point.

Having reached this stage we want to draw a comparison between the quantum theory of light and the corpuscular theory of Newton. We notice that in both theories light is considered as consisting of particles. According to Newton the light particle in a diffraction experiment at a slit is forced to choose another path by the edge of the slit; what then is changed if we put another slit further along the screen: the light particle does not become aware of the second slit, at any rate much less so than of the slit through which it goes. The quantum theory does not really know the concept of 'the path of a photon'; photons manifest themselves at a place where one goes and sits with a detector (a photocell, a sensitive plate); what happens between the detector and the source is described by the wave theory. We see that Newton's theory as such cannot explain Young's interference experiment; the quantum theory has no difficulty in doing so.

Apart from its intensity (or amplitude) the wave field at a particular place is characterised by its state of polarisation. How do we explain this in the quantum theory? Suppose we perform the following experiment: the photon comes flying in towards a Nicol, that is, a crystal polariser which only allows light oscillating in one direction through. Quantum mechanically this is to be expressed as follows: consider the allowed direction and the forbidden directions of oscillation of a Nicol as two mutually exclusive states (the hallmark of exclusiveness is here that the two states will not interfere). If now the light wave to which the photon belongs has a direction of polarisation of which the component q oscillates in the allowed direction of the Nicol and the component p in the forbidden one (see figure 150) then the probability that the photon will be transmitted through the Nicol is equal to $\frac{q^2}{p^2 + q^2}$, and the probability that it is not transmitted is $\frac{p^2}{p^2 + q^2}$. We say that the photon is in a mixed state which is composed of the allowed and unallowed directions of oscillation in the ratio $q:p$. Thus the polarisation of light also fits into the scheme of the quantum theory: the concept of choice or probability which is lacking in classical physics is directly applicable to it.

53 Lasers

A modern development in optics which we shall not allow to go unmentioned here is the laser. The name of this apparatus is an acronym for 'light amplification by stimulated emission of radiation'. We now want to explain what is meant by stimulated emission. First we describe a little more closely the construction of the apparatus. In figure 151 we see a diagram of it. In essence it consists of two mirrors opposite each other (thus really a Fabry-Perot interferometer!) between which there is an intensifying medium. One might say that this is a peculiar thing: a material which *intensifies* light instead of absorbing it! But more of this later; let us

Figures 151 and 152. *Left* The principle of the laser.
M shows the position of the intensifying medium made up
of atoms which send out photons (arrows).
Right Two energy levels of an atom. E_2 is the excited level,
E_1 the ground state. The possibilities are: (*A*) absorption of
a photon, (*B*) stimulated emission, (*C*) spontaneous emission.

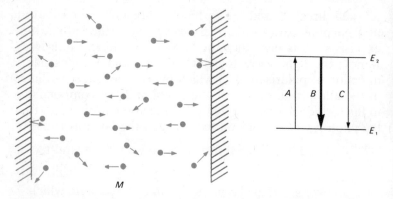

first assume that we can make such intensifying medium.
Light which is reflected backwards and forwards between the
mirrors loses at each reflection a little bit of its energy,
because the mirrors absorb and transmit some of the light.
We try now to make the intensification in the medium so large
that these losses are recovered during the passage of the wave
through the medium. If we reach this goal we then possess an
apparatus which can produce light (the light that is transmitted through the mirrors), while we do not put any light into it.

But in order to start the apparatus one does have to have
some light between the mirrors. Suppose we have atoms at
our disposal which have two energy levels (see figure 152).
We now see to it that the largest fraction of these atoms
arrives at the upper level. Such an atom is then in a position
to emit a photon $h\nu$ when it falls back into the lower level.
One must have

$$E_2 - E_1 = h\nu$$

which determines the frequency. Since there are many atoms
in the upper level, there will be many photons released
between the mirrors. These photons go in all directions; some

of them are reflected between the mirrors backwards and forwards and remain in the neighbourhood of the atoms. We have already said that an atom in an energy level higher than the ground state (which is the lowest possible energy level in which the atom normally is, like a stone at the bottom of a pit) is in a position to emit radiation. It does this normally after a short time (this time varies for most atoms between one hundred thousandths (10^{-5}) and one milliardth (10^{-9}) of a second) and thereby falls back to the ground state. This process is called 'spontaneous emission of the photon'.* It turns out that an atom emits photons much more quickly when there are many photons in its neighbourhood, than when it is on its own. The atom is *stimulated* to *emission* of the photon in the presence of this other radiation field. We therefore distinguish two kinds of emission: 'spontaneous' and 'stimulated'. In stimulated emission the emitted photon is identical to those which instigated its emission.

Between the mirrors of the laser-interferometer there are principally those photons present which are reflected backwards and forwards between the mirrors; in other words, in the laser, that radiation field can remain in existence for which the half wavelength fits precisely a whole number of times

---

* When separate atoms in some substance are excited, and shortly thereafter emit a photon, we speak of *fluorescence* (section 13). Laser materials are thus fluorescent media. When the emission of the photon takes place long after the excitation (as in the luminous paint on the hands of an alarm clock), one talks of *phosphorescence*. Both concepts are encompassed by the word *luminescence*. When the excitation occurs through the absorption of light, as happens in the ruby crystal, the luminescent light always has a longer wavelength than the incoming light (the emitted photon cannot have more energy than the one absorbed, and therefore has a smaller frequency). One can see this, for example in the luminous paints used on posters: they are mostly red (the longest wavelengths of the visible light). See also section 13.

between the two mirrors (see figure 146a). These kinds of photons are the ones most seen by atoms and, therefore, also the ones most sent out in stimulated emission. If we now see to it that there are enough of these 'good' photons, then there is always light going backwards and forwards between the mirrors and, therefore, laser light can go through the mirrors and be emitted outwards. This is achieved by continuously bringing more atoms to the upper energy level. To do this when one uses a gas as medium between the two mirrors. one allows an electric discharge to go through the gas. With a ruby laser, where the medium is a solid, the atoms are excited by the light from a flashlamp.

A laser, therefore, emits an intense beam of identical photons; in wave-language this means that the laser light is coherent. Therefore, one can use it for all sorts of interference experiments and for telecommunication (where it serves as a 'carrier wave'). Furthermore the wavefront coming out of the laser can be focused to a tiny point; this property and the large energy of the laser ray are used in a technique for making small holes, 'microwells', and in the performance of some eye operations.

In figure 153b we show a photograph of the helium-neon gas laser which emits a bright red beam ($\lambda = 633$ nm). The gas mixture is kept in a tube of pyrex glass F on which there are flat polished windows; these are covered with a coating in order to reduce the loss of light through reflection. The thick tube above it contains a reserve quantity of helium and neon gas; to the left and upper right one sees the electrodes of the gas discharge. Finally to the left and right one sees the mirrors; the laser beam between the mirrors is made visible by blowing smoke into it.

Figure 153a. Light from an argon-ion laser falls on a grating. Different orders of diffraction are visible.

242

Figure 153b. A gas laser in the laboratory.

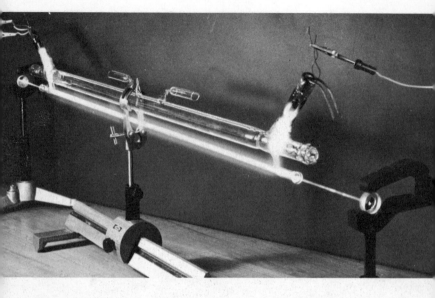

54 A cautious conclusion

We end this book with a couple of remarks about the problem stated at the beginning. We there set ourselves the task of giving an answer to the question 'what is light'?

In order to learn what this question implies we first gave a survey of the more important properties of light, such as these have been discovered experimentally by the scientists. In our description we used the hypothesis: light is a three dimensional transversal wave motion, and with this we obtained more or less satisfactory explanations of the phenomena we described.

The rest of the book, approximately from section 37 onwards, we devoted to the widening of the basis of our hypothesis. To this purpose we tried to give a review of the light theories which are used in modern science. The most important of these are the electromagnetic wave theory of Maxwell and the quantum theory. The remarkable thing is that these two theories do not exclude one another; the photons correspond altogether very nicely with the intensity distribution such as it is given by Maxwell's theory.

The development of science since Newton's time gives the following overall picture: if an established theory is overtaken by a new model, then the new model is more general, and includes the old. This does not mean that the old theory now is false; but only that the new one is more accurate or covers more cases. This leads us to the question: when then can one say that a theory in science has been shown to be valid? Strictly speaking never; one can, after all, never know whether there is not one experiment which might give the 'wrong' answer. The premises of a theory can never include all reality. Therefore, we must be careful in our judgment. This caution guides us now when considering the value of the answer that we have given here to the question 'what is light'? As an answer we have given a theory. That is the only thing a physicist can do. 'But what really is light?' one is asked; 'Give us a short answer in a few words'. Then we are tonguetied. To give such an answer one would have to be a poet.

Returning to the prosaic science we ask ourselves, 'Is our theory satisfactory'? If the reader has swallowed what we have told him so far, he may well answer 'yes'. The phenomena which we have described (superficially at any rate) found a ready explanation in the framework of the theory we used. But it remains possible that new experiments will give the theoreticians grey hairs. Furthermore when one goes

244

deeper into the matter than we have done here difficulties in the theory of light do emerge. Particularly in the field of the coherence of light sources, and in the field of the foundations of quantum theory there are still unanswered questions.

Apart from them there are, however, also problems which challenge the optician through their complexity. To name but a few: the motion of light through turbulent media, the electromagnetic explanation of diffraction phenomena, the correct connection between colour and spectral distribution, and the general theory of lens systems. It is enough to make one modest: we know quite a bit but we do not know all that much. We therefore leave the reader free to say, whenever he is asked 'What is light'? 'Well, that is quite simple: it is what you see'.

Further reading

The following short bibliography is recommended:

R. W. Ditchburn   *Light*
                         Blackie & Sons, London, 1963.

M. Cagney   *Atlas Optischer Erscheinunger*
M. Françon   Springer, Berlin, 1962.
J. C. Thrierr

A. A. Michelson   *Light Waves and their Uses*
                         University of Chicago Press,
                         Chicago, 1961.

A. A. Michelson   *Studies in Optics*
                         University of Chicago Press,
                         Chicago, 1962.

M. Minnaert   *Light and Colour in the Open Air*
                         Bell & Sons, London, 1959.
                         Clarke, Irwin & Co. Ltd.,
                         Toronto, 1959.

I. Newton   *Optics*
                         Dover Publications,
                         New York, 1952.

Acknowledgments

I am deeply indebted to Messrs P. Waasdorp and H. van Nes for their help with the diagrams, which were devised at the Physical Laboratory of the Technological University at Delft. I am also grateful to Design Practitioners Ltd for preparing the final artwork.

Professor A. C. S. van Heel

The manuscript of this book was completed shortly before the sudden death of my colleague and former teacher, Professor A.C.S. van Heel, on 18 May 1966. Professor van Heel was both a great teacher and a great exponent of the science of optics. For forty years he lectured at the Technological University at Delft, when he did research on the theory of aberrations, optical projection, and precision measurements. Throughout his life he was devoted to the advancement of his chosen science and kept in close contact with fellow-workers in Holland and other countries, being for many years co-editor of the International Commission of Optics and of the journal *Optica Acta*.

C. H. F. VELZEL

252

World University Library

Books published or in preparation

Economics and Social Studies

The World Cities
Peter Hall, *London*

The Economics of Underdeveloped Countries
Jagdish Bhagwati,
M.I.T.

Development Planning
Jan Tinbergen,
Rotterdam

Leadership in New Nations
T. B. Bottomore,
Vancouver

Human Communication
J. L. Aranguren,
Madrid

Education in the Modern World
John Vaizey, *Oxford*

Soviet Economics
Michael Kaser, *Oxford*

Decisive Forces in World Economics
J. L. Sampedro, *Madrid*

Money
Roger Opie, *Oxford*

The Sociology of Africa
Jacques Maquet, *Paris*

Science and Anti-Science
T. R. Gerholm,
Stockholm

Key Issues in Criminology
Roger Hood, *Durham*

Society and Population
E. A. Wrigley,
Cambridge

History

The Old Stone Age
François Bordes,
Bordeaux

The Evolution of Ancient Egypt
Werner Kaiser, *Berlin*

The Emergence of Greek Democracy
W. G. Forrest, *Oxford*

The Roman Empire
J. P. V. D. Balsdon,
Oxford

Muhammad and the Conquests of Islam
Francesco Gabrieli,
Rome

The Civilisation of Charlemagne
Jacques Boussard,
Poitiers

The Crusades
Geo Widengren,
Uppsala

The Medieval Italian Republics
D. P. Waley, *London*

The Medieval Economy
Georges Duby,
Aix-en-Provence

The Ottoman Empire
Halil Inalcik, *Ankara*

Humanism in the Renaissance
S. Dresden, *Leyden*

The Rise of Toleration
Henry Kamen, *Warwick*

The Scientific Revolution 1500-1700
Hugh Kearney, *Sussex*

The Dutch Republic
C. H. Wilson,
Cambridge

The Left in Europe
David Caute, *Oxford*

The Rise of the Working Class
Jürgen Kuczynski,
Berlin

Chinese Communism
Robert North, *Stanford*

Arab Nationalism
Sylvia Haim, *London*

The Culture of Japan
Mifune Okumura,
Kyoto

The History of Persia
Jean Aubin, *Paris*

Language and Literature

The Birth of Western Languages
Philippe Wolff, *Toulouse*

A Model of Language
E. M. Uhlenbeck, *Leyden*

French Literature
Raymond Picard, *Paris*

Russian Writers and Society 1825-1904
Ronald Hingley, *Oxford*

Satire
Matthew Hodgart, *Sussex*

The Romantic Century
Robert Baldick, *Oxford*

The Arts

The Language of Modern Art
Ulf Linde, *Stockholm*

Architecture since 1945
Bruno Zevi, *Rome*

Twentieth Century Music
H. H. Stuckenschmidt, *Berlin*

Aesthetic Theories since 1850
J. F. Revel, *Paris*

Art Nouveau
S. Tschudi Madsen, *Oslo*

Academic Painting
Gerald Ackerman, *Stanford*

Palaeolithic Cave Art
P. J. Ucko and A. Rosenfeld, *London*

Primitive Art
Eike Haberland, *Mainz*

Romanesque Art
Carlos Cid Priego, *Madrid*

Expressionism
John Willett, *London*

Philosophy and Religion

Christianity
W. O. Chadwick, *Cambridge*

Monasticism
David Knowles, *London*

Judaism
J. Soetendorp, *Amsterdam*

The Modern Papacy
K. O. von Aretin, *Göttingen*

Witchcraft
Lucy Mair, *London*

Sects
Bryan Wilson, *Oxford*

Physical Science and Mathematics

Energy
Etienne Fischhoff, *Paris*

Crystals and Minerals
Hugo Strunz, *Berlin*

The Quest for Absolute Zero
K. Mendelssohn, *Oxford*

Particles and Accelerators
Robert Gouiran, *C.E.R.N., Geneva*

What is Light?
A. C. S. van Heel and C. H. F. Velzel, *Eindhoven*

Mathematics Observed
Hans Freudenthal, *Utrecht*

Waves and Corpuscles
J. L. Andrade e Silva and G. Lochak, *Paris*. Introduction by Louis de Broglie

Science and Statistics
S. Sagoroff, *Vienna*

New Mathematics
R. Faure, *Paris*

Applied Science

Words and Waves
A. H. W. Beck,
Cambridge

The Science of Decision-making
A. Kaufmann, *Paris*

Bionics
Lucien Gerardin, *Paris*

Metals and Civilisation
R. W. Cahn, *Sussex*

Bioengineering
H. S. Wolff, *London*

Data Study
J. L. Jolley, *London*

Psychology and Human Biology

The Molecules of Life
Gisela Nass, *Munich*

The Variety of Man
J. P. Garlick, *London*

Eye and Brain
R. L. Gregory,
Edinburgh

The Ear and the Brain
E. C. Carterette,
U.C.L.A.

The Biology of Work
O. G. Edholm, *London*

The Psychology of Attention
Anne Treisman, *Oxford*

Psychoses
H. J. Bochnik,
Hamburg

Neuropsycho-pharmacology
A. M. Ernst, *Utrecht*

The Psychology of Fear and Stress
J. A. Gray, *Oxford*

Psychosomatic Medicine
A. Mitscherlich,
Heidelberg

Child Development
Philippe Muller,
Neuchâtel

Man and Disease
Gernot Rath, *Göttingen*

The Doctor and the Patient
P. Lain Entralgo,
Madrid

Chinese Medicine
P. Huard and M. Wong,
Paris

Mind in the Universe
Gosta Ehrensvard,
Lund

Zoology and Botany

Animal Communication
J. M. Cullen, *Oxford*

Mimicry
Wolfgang Wickler,
Seewiesen

Migration
Gustaf Rudebeck,
Stockholm

Lower Animals
Martin Wells,
Cambridge

The World of an Insect
Rémy Chauvin,
Strasbourg

Biological Rhythms
Janet Harker,
Cambridge

Life in the Sea
Gunnar Thorson,
Elsinore

Primates
François Bourlière,
Paris

The Conservation of Nature
C. Delamare
Deboutteville, *Paris*

The Variation of Plants
S. M. Walters and
D. Briggs, *Cambridge*

Plant Cells
R. Buvat, *Paris*

The Age of the Dinosaurs
Björn Kurtén, *Helsinki*

Earth Sciences and Astronomy

The Structure of the Universe
E. L. Schatzman, *Paris*

Climate and Weather
H. Flohn, *Bonn*

Anatomy of the Earth
André Cailleux, *Paris*

Sun, Earth and Radio
J. A. Ratcliff,
Cambridge